THE WAYS
OF LOVE

To Marion
From Fran
With Love
Valentines Day, 1965

THE

WAYS

OF

LOVE

Eleven Romances

of Medieval France

NORMA LORRE GOODRICH

BEACON PRESS

CONTENTS

INTRODUCTION   vii

I. THE LIFE OF SAINT ALEXIS. *Anonymous.*   3

II. THE ROMANCE OF GIRART DE VIENE. *Bertrand de Bar-sur-Aube.*   21

III. THE SWAN KNIGHT. *Anonymous.*   49

IV. ELIDUC. *Marie de France.*   71

V. YONEC. *Marie de France.*   101

VI. THE ROMANCE OF TRISTRAN. *Béroul.*   117

VII. EREC AND ENIDE. *Chrétien de Troyes.*   137

VIII. THE ROMANCE OF THE CHÂTELAIN OF COUCY. *Anonymous.*   159

IX. THE ROMANCE OF THE STORY OF THE GRAIL. *Robert de Boron.*   201

X. AUCASSIN AND NICOLETTE. *Anonymous.*   217

XI. THE LAY OF A SHADOW. *Jehan Renart.*   253

NOTES ON THE SOURCES   275

*This book is dedicated to Mr. and
Mrs. Henry Barnes and to the Faculty
of the Rudolf Steiner School in New
York City because their lives and
works are the best examples of love
I have known.*

INTRODUCTION

Opening a book is like entering. Entering is like passing through a doorway into a quiet room where strange persons sit waiting for us to come. Entering is like walking through a gate into a flowering garden where people we have never seen before and whose names we do not know come forward to meet us with smiles on their faces. Once we have opened their books, passed into the quiet of their studies, entered their flowering gardens, they speak briefly to us of the best things they have been able to find out in all their lives. The strangest people we will meet as we open this book are the authors. Some of them condensed the total experience of their entire lives into twenty pages ending with a period. Their book went to a scribe who copied it on expensive vellum as best he could, or as fast as he could, at so much a word.

As a we turn the pages of this book, we meet French writers of romances from the eleventh, the twelfth, and the thirteenth centuries. They cannot ever be properly introduced, for in many cases we do not even know their names. We can only describe them as, for instance, the man who turned into Old French *The Life of Saint Alexis*. It must be that because he felt so deeply the urgency to tell this story to others who could not read it, he did his best to re-create the pitiful life of Alexis, whom he loved centuries after his death. In other cases, we can at best name a few names: Bertrand from Bar-sur-Aube, a small town on the frontiers of Champagne and Burgundy; Chrétien from Troyes, Champagne's ancient capital, named for a still more ancient Troy; Jehan Renart (John Fox?); Robert de Boron, perhaps from Montbéliard in eastern France; *the*

Béroul who wrote the earliest French version of *Tristran*; Marie called "from France" because, an expatriate, she probably made her home in England. Our other five writers of romance in the romance tongue of Old French remain to this day anonymous. They are like strangers we meet on the ocean, or, these days, in the air. Because we are nameless strangers to them, they tell us in a few minutes the whole story of their loves and their lives, in accents they would not for the world have their nearest and dearest hear, and then rise nameless with a smile, anxious to pass to their destinations. What they have said, and the comments we have made as punctuation, have already become a part of our lives. We have been enriched. It all happened too fast for us to have become bored. They have been released. Yet both are obliged.

The author, like the speaker, is obliged because he has been temporarily released from his ceaseless wonderment about love, about people, about the world, about himself. The reader or the listener is obliged because he has been able to fill in from his own experience and his own acquisition of certain knowledge all the gaps in the conversation. Those strange authors we meet in this book were primarily concerned with love; it was their emotion *par excellence*.

Where the medieval writers of epics had raised to the skies the heroic names and deeds of Roland and Charlemagne, other medieval authors found themselves not so much interested in a man's world of military feats and empire building as they were in a man's love for a woman, and her love for him. As Gustave Cohen pointed out in his book on medieval art, these authors were concerned with quest, such as the "quest" for personal happiness, rather than the "conquest" of the external world. Such authors, it has often been demonstrated, wrote for women also and were even commissioned to write by women. They wrote in some measure for noble ladies whose lords and husbands were absent in the Crusades. They tried to appeal to an elegant and a refined and a stable feudal society intent upon culture and the cultivation of the arts of peace. In any case, authors such as the ones we shall meet in this book discovered that love was one of the best subjects for treatment in the romance tongue as opposed to Latin. A love story well told, they found, was apt to find a receptive audience. Most people who heard it, listened. Most listeners were, or had been, or wanted to be, in love. Those who heard the story knew much from actual experience about the havoc caused by unrequited love, by jealousy, by infidelity, by interference and opposition, and by inconstancy. Everyone had felt some kind of love. The authors were enchanted to discover that as they told the story, the listeners collaborated. Once strangers, they became friends.

After they had borrowed the theme of love from the *troubadours,* the writers of romances showed themselves astonishingly versatile, astonishingly agile in the great variety and the many variations of which they were capable. In the eleven romances translated from Old French in this volume, for example, one author will understand that the love of God reigns so supremely in the heart of one young man that he will reject his bride on their wedding night, spurn his parents, his home, and his wealth to set forth on the quest of absolute love. A second author will study the vengeance taken by a woman whose love is spurned by a young adventurer. A third will dedicate to his own lady a romance in which adulterous love leads a guilty and unrepentant pair to their deaths. A fourth will show how a good wife, whose husband has been unfaithful, acted in such a situation. A fifth romance will revolve about the longing for love of a young girl married against her will to a cruel old man. A great psychologist, Chrétien de Troyes, will tackle the thorny problem of a how a young husband coped with the incipient disillusionment his young wife felt after marriage. There is included also a fragment from *Tristran,* that most puzzling and intriguing story in which the renegade lovers find their tragic love beyond the confines of society too hard to bear. Another novelist will show how a jealous mother-in-law can destroy a marriage. Still another will attempt to explain love as directed towards the quest for the Holy Grail. In *The Lay of a Shadow* a consummate medieval artist will study systematic seduction, and the battle of the sexes. Another romance will tell again its familiar tale of a poor orphan who has only her frailty, her beauty, and her love as weapons against a cruel, cruel world.

Many poets of the Middle Ages associated love with chivalry and with courtesy. By its very nature, they thought, love implied self-sacrifice, self-effacement, and the placing of the beloved's welfare first. Love established a relationship between men and women in which each was concerned first for the other. Both were bound by courtesy. According to the laws of love, a knight devoted himself to one woman whom he swore to respect and to obey. He set upon himself the task of winning her love by manly exercises, by personal accomplishments, by complete discretion and secrecy, and by their shared delight in poetry and music. Thus her constancy, her tenderness, her grace, her wit, her charm, and her beauty complemented his physical strength, his achievements, his artistic powers, his resourcefulness, his adoration, and his tenderness. Both were bound by their idea of honor. Both were chivalrous. The suitor might be an unmarried knight, and the lady to whom he paid court a married lady.

The lady was given a name, or she was a flower, such as the marguerite. Her colors might be sapphire blue, which tokened truth; she was thus true-blue. Gold, the color of her hair or the golden light of happiness she shed, or the gold of a ring or a tomb might be associated with her. Her mourning lover, perpetually pleading, might wear black for his aching heart. On May Day garlands were woven for the lady's hair while her courtiers wore green for their maying jaunts into the forests and fields. Love was associated with springtime and flowers. The lady rode a dappled palfrey, held her favorite falcon on her wrist, or was drawn in an open chariot hitched to two white horses. She customarily received a new pledge of love on Saint Valentine's Day. Medieval ladies, just like modern ones, were very fond of stories, of dancing and singing, of parties of all kinds and of festivals, of games, of beautiful clothes, and of travel. The deportment of ladies as well as that of knights was ruled by conventions.

In the event of broken laws, sanctions were imposed. A man could see his castle razed to the ground, his title lost to himself and to his heirs, and himself obliged to set out on foot for the Holy Land. Immorality in women was punished either by society's disapprobation or even by death at their husbands' hands. Women in high stations who fell into political disgrace could be and were tried for witchcraft, and subsequently destituted and exiled. Probably more can be learned about women in the Middle Ages, however, from reading romances than in any other way. Aside from certain vital statistics concerning great queens, very little is known about the women of that period. One is reduced to staring at their faces on cathedrals and tombs, and noting their styles of dress and hair on the colorful miniatures of the period.

The writers of romance in this volume wrote for such ladies at such a time. They were not necessarily concerned with ideal love as celebrated in medieval songs and poems. The poets could be concerned with ideal love which knew no barriers, was no respecter of persons, and which did not ordinarily exist in the everyday, working world. Such love was preferably unrequited. It was preferably a thirst for the transcendent and for the unattainable. It was a desire rather than a passion, a search rather than a fulfillment, a worship of the unknown peak of perfection—snow-clad and tantalizing. The novelists, by nature human beings subject to life around them (and they lived far below the summits of Parnassus), were impelled to draw from life situations. Therefore, although "courteous" love was ideally addressed by a young knight to a completely unyielding married lady, other situations replaced in romances this ideal and poetic stalemate. Certain married ladies yielded to importunities. Certain husbands, not supposed to be characters in the story, crept in to steal the show, as in the case of King Mark of Cornwall. Certain knights were inconsistent with their vows of eternal love. In other cases, the young lady had to take steps to help love along, if she were ever to be happily married. While Dante united ideal love with the love of God, medieval French novelists chose another fork in the trail, and studied love upon an earthly path. All along this path they erected signs in large letters: DANGER!

The medieval writers of romances, anonymous and obscure poets as they are, wait to be introduced in the open pages of a book. Although they are strangers and foreigners, they still smile at us today with their wise and friendly faces. They made their contribution to humanity by studying this aspiration towards love which rises in every human heart. Then, as now, marriages failed, Then, as now, sincere and honest people went to their graves without having found that love which could make their lives worthwhile. Even then the paths of life were beset by pitfalls which it was incumbent upon the novelist to know so that his reader could at least be forewarned. Then, as now, novelists seeking in their own way a force which could defeat death concluded that it was love. They knew that however variously they treated the subject, they would find a sympathetic audience eager to hear them out. They took the first step when their hands lifted their pens.

The next step is ours: mine because these eleven stories were selected for translation, and yours to judge their interest, their worth, their pertinence, and their application to modern life. As far as their choosing is concerned, it was done primarily on the basis of pure pleasure. This is the criterion which I believe each one of the authors would have applied first. These were not necessarily learned authors; or, if they were learned, they took great pains to make it appear that they wrote first of all to please, and secondarily so that their stories would not be forgotten. For reasons of his own, in other words, each found his story eminently worth recording. Some of them were themselves amused at the yarn they were spinning. Others were earnest to the point of being devout. All were skilled in their craft. Some were cultivated, refined, and sophisticated. Others were coarse. They recognized as a group many ways of love, all of them equally worthy of literature: a love of purely physical origin, a love pursued in terms of siege and defense, a love more like an aspiration for the absolute, a love which was a burden imposed by external force, a dream of love, a passionate love which seems to have been related to a disregard for life, a love born at first sight, and a self-sacrificing love.

Although these writers were not necessarily French in the modern sense of the term, they all wrote in Old French. A sample of their actual words is given in each case, either in the text itself or in the accompanying notes. All wrote entirely in verse, with the exception of the author of *Aucassin and Nicolette,* who alternated prose with verse. In France, prose began to replace verse during the course of the thirteenth century. These writers, then, were not novelists in our meaning of the word since the first real novels as we know them date from such a work as *Lazarillo de Tormes* in the sixteenth century. Their romances were, however, ancestors of the modern novel. Their use of love as a central theme originated in France whence it spread via England to America, just as did the French creation of "courteous" love, or love associated with courts and chivalry.

Paying court to a highborn medieval lady often required years of service concentrated upon that suit. A practitioner of the art of love in medieval literature often borrowed phraseology and imagery from the law courts, often spoke of Love's court where Cupid presided, and where the lover began his contract. The successful prosecution of his suit required on the lover's part an education in courtly manners and court procedure, the ability to compose love poetry, and the leisure to dance attendance upon the lady so importuned. Such love was an occupation of courtiers and courts, an art in which the idle rich became proficient. A part of the stigma attached to romances, and to the reading of romances even in the Middle Ages, a stigma which perhaps continues even to this day, may very well have had its origin in these two facts: romances tended to prefer speaking of profane love that was as often as not illicit, and courtly love was an occupation of the idle rich.

In modern America "courting" is not confined to any particular segment of the population. The ways of love are open to all. Love is still born of Beauty or of beauty. Ladies are still courted. Vows are still exchanged like rings. Cupid still fires his arrows into hearts on Saint Valentine's Day. Love is still associated with springtime, with music, with birds, and with flowers. And so even today, we can enter the quiet studies and the flowering gardens of the medieval men and women of letters as if into familiar surroundings. Not only have our eyes seen and admired the other works of art, the paintings, the tapestries, the sculpture, and the cathedrals their contemporaries created—our ears are tuned to their phrases as perhaps nowhere else in the world today. Our lives were shaped in some measure by their words and by their thoughts. They, now dead, are still our teachers and guides in the ways of love. When they wrote, they were enthusiastic, wise, witty, thoughtful, experienced, and generous people. As we read, we can hardly think of these authors as either ancient or foreign; they are vibrant colorful men and women with words to say we might want to hear, with ideas we might want to discuss with them in our own quiet gardens and flowering rooms.

N. L. G.

THE WAYS
OF LOVE

I

THE LIFE OF SAINT ALEXIS

Anonymous

ELEVENTH CENTURY

 N THE DAYS of the ancients the age was good, for then there were faith, justice, and love; there was also belief, of which there is hardly any left now; it is all changed now—it has lost its color; it will never again be as it was in the days of the ancients. . . . At the time of Noah and at the time of Abraham and at the time of David, whom God loved very much, the age was good; it will never be so worthy again. It is old now and fragile, everything goes into decline, thus it has become worse, all good stands still.

After the time when God came to save us, our ancestors received the Christian faith.

Then there was a lord in the city of Rome. He was a powerful man, of the high nobility; I tell you this because I want to speak of this man's son. Eufemium—this was the father's name—was a count of Rome, among the better who then were in that city. Above all his peers the emperor loved him. He therefore took to wife a worthy and esteemed lady from the most noble of the whole land. Then they lived together a long time, but had no children; this weighed upon them heavily. Both sincerely call upon God: "Oh! heavenly King, by thine commandment, give us a child according to Thy will!"

So sincerely did they pray to God in all humility that He gave fertility to the wife. He gave them a son. Thus they were very grateful; they brought the child into a new life by holy baptism. According to the Christian faith, they gave him a beautiful name. He was baptized and named Alexis.

His mother who bore him reared him gently. Then his good father put him in school; he learned so many letters that he was well supplied; then the child will serve the emperor. When his father saw that he would have no other child but this one alone whom he dearly loved, he thought to himself that his son should take a wife during his lifetime; therefore he bought the daughter of a noble free man.

The maiden was of very high parentage, the daughter of a count of the city of Rome; he has no other child—he wishes to honor her much. The two fathers go together to speak nicely. Sir Alexis marries her beautifully; but of such an arrangement he wanted nothing; wholly has he his thoughts towards God. When the day passes and it was night, the father says: "Son, for now to bed with your wife at the commandment of Heaven."

The boy does not want to irritate his father; he goes into the chamber with his noble wife. When he sees the bed, looks at the maiden, then he remembers his Heavenly Lord whom he holds dearer than any earthly possession. "Oh, God," says he, "how strong sin oppresses me! If I do not flee now, I fear greatly that I shall lose Thee!"

When they had both been put alone in the bedroom, Sir

Alexis began to call upon his wife; he began to blame mortal life much and to show her the truth of heavenly life, but he is anxious to turn away from her.

"Do you hear me, maiden? Hold as your spouse Him who redeemed us with His precious blood. In this century there is no such thing as perfect love; life is fragile, honor is not enduring, all joy turns back to great sadness." When he had shown her all his reasoning, then he confided into her care his sword and the ring with which he had wed her. Then he issued forth from the chamber of his father; in the dead of night he left the land.

Then, traveling along, he went straight to the sea, the ship is ready where he was to embark, he pays his price and goes aboard. They hoist their sails, let her run to sea and make a landfall where God desires to lead them. Straight at Lalice, which was a very beautiful city, the bark arrives safely. Sir Alexis went ashore, but I do not know how long he stays; wherever he may be, he never ceases serving God. From there he went to the city of Alsis because of a statue which he heard said the angels had made by order of God in the name of the Virgin who brought us salvation, Saint Mary who bore the Lord God.

All the wealth he had brought with him he shared in the city of Alsis—such large alms that nothing remained for himself; he gives away to the poor wherever he can find them; he wishes not to be encumbered with any goods. When he had shared his goods with them, Sir Alexis sat down among the poor, asked for alms when God sent him any. From this he kept only enough to care for his own body; if there is anything left over, he returns it to the poor.

Now I will come back to his father and mother and to the spouse he espoused. When they knew it, that he had gone away, it was a great mourning they made and a loud outcry throughout all the city. The father says: "Dear son, now have I lost you!"

6

The mother replies, "Alas! what has become of him!"

The wife says, "Sin took him away from me! Oh! dear friend, how little I had you! Now I am so sad that I cannot be more so."

Then the father takes from his best servants and has them quest for his child across numerous lands, all the way to Alsis two went traveling; there they found Sir Alexis staying, but they recognized neither his face nor his aspect. The child had altered his tender flesh, the servants of his father did not therefore know him, even to him they gave alms, he received them like the other brothers. They did not recognize him, and immediately they went on their way.

They did not recognize him nor did they know him. Sir Alexis thanked God in heaven for the alms he received from his own servants. He was their lord, now he is their debtor. I cannot say to you how joyous he was. . . . They went home to Rome, the city. They announce to the father that they could not find him. It is not necessary to ask whether or not he was sad.

The good mother begins to go out of her mind and to mourn often for her dear son. "Alexis, son, why did your mother bear you? You ran from me, and I am again become grief-stricken. I do not know the place, I do not know the country where I may go to seek you; I am all lost. Never shall I be joyous, dear son, nor your father either." Full of sadness she entered the chamber; she tore it apart so that nothing remained; no tapestries remained, no adornments remained. She turned her mind towards such a sadness that never since that day did she ever behave joyously.

"Chamber," she said, "never will you be redecorated, never shall happiness have stayed in you!" She wrecked that bedroom as if an army had sacked it; she let it hang in rags and tatters; she turned her great honor into great dole. In her grief the mother sat down, on the ground.

Then surely this way spoke the wife of Alexis: "Lady," she

7

said, "what a great loss have I! From now on I will live like the mourning dove. Since I do not have your son, I wish to be together with you."

The mother said: "If you wish to stay with me, then I will keep you, for the love of Alexis. Never will you suffer any ill from which I cannot heal you. Let us weep together for the loss of our friend—you for your lord—I for my dear son."

It cannot be otherwise; they turn it over in their thoughts, but they cannot forget their pain.

In the city of Alsis Sir Alexis serves his Lord with all his might. His enemy can get no hold on him. There is nothing to be said of him for a period of seventeen years except that he mortified his body for the Lord his God. Neither for friendship, nor for a friend, nor for a woman, nor for any honors he could inherit does he desire to return while he still has life. Only when he had so strengthened his heart that henceforward he will not leave Alsis, God then made the statue speak to a servant who was serving at the altar. He commanded this to him: "Call the man of God."

This the statue said: "Have the man of God come, for he has well and graciously served God, and he is worthy to enter paradise."

The man goes and searches for him, but he does not know how to recognize the holy man about whom the statue spoke. The sacristan returns to the statue in the minster. "For sure," he says, "I do not know whom to recognize."

The statue replies, "It is he who is seated near the door, he who is near God and near the Kingdom of Heaven, in no way whatsoever does he wish to separate himself from them."

This man goes and searches and has him come into the minster. Thus the news spreads over all the country that this statue spoke for Alexis. Then all, the great and the humble, all pray that he may take pity on them.

When he sees this, that they wish to honor him, he says:

8

"Certainly, I do not have to remain here any longer; I do not wish to be encumbered all over again with this honor. . . ." At midnight he flees from the city. His voyage takes him back to Lalice. Sir Alexis went aboard ship, they had a fair wind, they let the ship sail. They hope to arrive at Tarsus, but it cannot be. He must go elsewhere. The wind bears them directly and straight for Rome. The ship of this holy man arrives at one of the ports which is near Rome.

When he sees his homeland, he fears deeply for himself because of his parents, that they may recognize him, that they may encumber him with the esteem of the century. "Oh, God!" he says, "beautiful King who governs all, if it had been pleasing to Thee, I would not have wished to be here. If my parents recognize me here in this country, they will take me by prayers or by force. If I believe in their words, they will draw me to perdition.

"Yet, in spite of this, my father longs for me. So does my mother more than any woman alive. I left my wife with them. Now I will not let them put me in their power. They will not recognize me. It has been so many days since they saw me."

He leaves the ship and goes directly and straight to Rome. He walks down the streets with which he once was so well acquainted. He sees one person and another, and then he meets his father. A great crowd of his men were together with him. He recognized him; by his true name he names him.

"Eufemium, good sir, wealthy man, for God's sake give me shelter in your house. Under your staircase make me a nook, for the love of your son, for whom you feel such grief; I am entirely broken in health. So feed me for the love of him."

When the father hears the appeal of his son, his eyes weep; he cannot refrain. "For the love of God and for my dear friend I will give you everything, my good man, as much as

9

you have asked: bed and lodging and bread and meat and wine. Oh, God," he said, "why have I not a servant who would attend to him! I would make him a free man."

There was such a one who came forward. "I," he said, "am one who will attend him by your orders. For the love of you I will endure the task." Then he led him directly under the flight of steps: he makes up a bed for him where he can rest; he prepares for him everything he needs. He does not wish to behave badly towards his lord; he cannot be blamed in any way.

Both father and mother saw him often, and also the maiden he married; in no way whatsoever did they ever recognize him, nor did Alexis ever tell them, nor did they ever ask what man he was and from what land he was. Oftentimes he saw them moaning and mourning and tenderly weeping the tears from their eyes, crying entirely for him, never for anyone else . . . Sir Alexis sees all this. . . . Under the stairs where he lies on his pallet, there they feed him with scraps from the table. He thus reduces his high lineage to great poverty. He does not want his mother to know it. He loves God more than all his relatives.

Out of the food which comes to him from the household he keeps only enough to sustain his body; if there is any left over, he returns it to beggars. He does not lay up a store to fatten his own body, but instead, he gives something to eat to the poor. He remains by preference in the holy church and takes communion every feast day. His counselor was always the Holy Writ. He wishes to bend all his strength to the service of God—in no fashion to deviate from it.

He leads joyously a life of poverty under the steps where he lies and resides. His father's slaves who serve in the household throw their wash water upon his head. He does not become angry, does not call them to task for this. They all sneer at him and consider him a fool. They throw water on him; thus they make his bed all wet. This most holy man in no way becomes irritated, but instead he prays to God that He pardon them through His mercy, for they know not what they do.

There he resides so for seventeen years. No one from among his own people recognizes him in any way. Nor did any man know his suffering, nor anything except the bed where he lay so long. He could not help them from knowing what was obvious.

For thirty-four years then he thus afflicted his body. God wishes to reward him for this devotion. His infirmities weigh most heavily upon him. He knows now that he must depart. He called his servant to him. "Good brother, search out ink and parchment for me, and a quill, I pray you, by your mercy." This man brings them to him; Alexis receives them. He writes a whole letter from himself, how he went away, and how he returned. He clasps the letter close to him, does not wish to show it for fear that they still may recognize him before he departs.... Sincerely he has commended himself to God. His end approaches, his body has become heavy, he ceases speaking totally.

In that week when he had to depart, there came three times in the city out of a holy church at the command of God a voice which summoned all the faithful there: the glory which God wishes to give him approaches. In a different voice were said other summonses: that they were seeking the man of God, who is in Rome, that they were praying to him that the city not collapse, that the people who dwelled in it not perish. All who heard these words stood still in great uncertainty.

Saint Innocent was then the high priest. Towards him came from that place both the rich and the poor, and they asked his counsel about this thing which they have heard, which discomforts them greatly. They are no longer looking for that hour when the earth swallows them up. The high priest and the emperor—one was named Arcadius and the other Honorius—and all the people in a common supplication pray God to give them counsel in this matter of a holy man through whom they will be healed. They plead that He, out of His accustomed goodness, teach them where they can find him.

Then a voice which made them comprehend: "Search in the house of Eufemium, for he is there. There you will find him."

Everyone turns away from there to the house of Sir Eufemium. Some people take it upon themselves to criticize him sharply: "You should have announced this thing to us, to all the people who were disheartened. So long have you hidden this man, so much have you sinned greatly."

Sir Eufemium begs their pardon like a man who does not know him, but they do not believe him. They went to his residence. Eufemium goes ahead of them to prepare his house. He inquires closely of all his minstrels. They answer that none of them knows him.

The high priest and the emperors seat themselves on their benches, pensive and weeping. All the other lords look upon them there. They pray to God that He will give them counsel in this matter of a holy man through whom they will be healed. During this time, as they are seated there, the soul severs itself from the body of Saint Alexis. Right straightaway it goes from there into paradise, towards the Lord whom he had so well served. (Oh! Heavenly Lord, Thou, make us come to Thee!)

The good servant who served him willingly announced this to his father Eufemium. He calls him softly and advises him so: "Sire," he says, "your ward is dead, and this much I can say: that he was a good Christian. I remained with him for a very long time. I truly cannot say he was faulty in any way, and this is my idea, that he is the man of God."

Eufemium all alone turned away from the hall, went to his son where he lay under the steps. . . He raises the sheets which covered him. He sees the beautiful and candid face of the holy man. This servant of God holds a letter in his hand, a letter where he told of his long sojourns. Eufemium wishes to know what the letter spells out. He wishes to take it and read; the dead man does not let go his fingers. Deeply disturbed, Eufemium returns to the high prelate.

"Now I have found what we sought so long. A pilgrim lies dead under my staircase. He is holding a letter, but I cannot take it out of his grip."

The prelate and the emperors come before him, throw themselves to the floor in prayer, cast their bodies into great torment. "Mercy on us. Mercy. Mercy, most saintly man. Truly we did not know you, nor do not know you now. Here before you kneel two sinners who by the grace of God are called emperors (for by His grace does He bestow honor upon us). We are the judges of this whole wide world; now we are in great need of your counsel.

"By right the prelate must govern the souls of men. That is his task which he has to perform. Out of your great good mercy, give him the letter. He will tell us what there will be written inside it. And may God grant that as of now we may because of it be healed."

The prelate extends his hand for the letter. Saint Alexis lets it go into his hand. He gives it to the prelate, who was the Pope of Rome. He does not read it, nor does he look at what is inside. First he hands it to a good and upright scholar. It was this scholar, this chancellor whose duty was such matters—it was he who read the letter. The others heard it. He it was who told them the name of this pearl of great price whom they had found there. He told them the names of his father and mother. He told them all that and from what parents he was.

And he told them how he fled over the sea, and how he was in the city of Alsis, and how God commanded the statue

13

to speak on his behalf, and how—because of the honor with which he did not wish to be heavily laden—he fled back once more into the city of Rome.

When the father heard what the letter said, he tore his white beard. "Oh, son," he said, "what a painful message! I was waiting for you to return to me in the hope that out of God's mercy you would be a comfort to me." Then the father began to cry aloud, "Alexis my son, what a sorrow has fallen upon me now! I had you ill tended under my steps! Alas, sinner that I am, how blinded I was! I saw you so many times, and even so was not able to recognize you. . . . Alexis, my son, what of your mourning mother! and of the great griefs she has endured for your sake, and all the fastings, and the thirsts she has withstood, and what of all the tears she has wept for your dear sake. This new bereavement will pierce right through her heart.

"Oh, son, for whom shall my great inheritances be, for whom my vast lands of which I had many, my great palaces in the city of Rome? For you I had burdened myself with these matters so that after my death you would be esteemed because of them. White is my head and sparse my beard. I only kept my great estate because of you. It was only for you, but you had no concern for all that. What a great pain has appeared before me now! Son, may your soul be absolved into heaven!

"It would have been fitting for you to have worn helmet and byrnie—to buckle on a sword like the other peers. You would have ruled over a large household. You would have borne the pennant of the emperor . . . just like your father and all those of your line. . . . In what pain and poverty did you live in strange lands! And of all this wealth, which by right should have been yours, you took little for your poor encampment. If such had been the will of God, you would have been lord over all of it."

Because of the pain which the father felt, his laments

14

were loud. And so the mother overheard him. She came running like a woman crazed, striking her palms against each other, shrieking, her hair falling down over her face. She sees her son dead and falls unconscious. Any person who could have seen her then expressing her bereavement—striking her chest, throwing her body about, tearing her hair, and cutting her cheeks with her nails, and kissing her dead son and putting her arms about him—no matter how hard-hearted such a person could be—he would have been melted to tears himself.

She tears out her hair and beats her chest; she inflicts her sorrow upon her very own flesh. "Ah! son," she says, "how you have hated me! And I, grieving over you, how blinded I was! I no more recognized you than as if I had never even seen you."

She screams and cries and the tears stream down her face. Without ceasing, she laments: "It was at an evil hour, beautiful son, that I bore you! Did you not feel pity for your mother? You saw me long for death because of you. What a marvel it is that pity did not move you! Alas! Wretched woman that I am, what a powerful misadventure was mine. Now I see lying dead my only child and descendant. My long years of waiting have led to this great loss! Why did I ever bear you, grieving, wretched woman that I am! What a great wonder it is that my heart can still beat!

"Alexis my son, what hardness of courage you had when you forsook your noble family! If only you had spoken to me of it, only one time! If only you had once comforted your unfortunate mother, who is so mournful. Dear son, then you would have gone at a good hour.

"Alexis my son, how soft your flesh used to be! In what sorrow did you spend your youth! Why did you run from me? I carried you in my belly, and God knows how afflicted I am utterly. Never, for man or for woman, will I ever be joyous again. . . . Before I had you, I was full of desire.

15

Before you were born, I was full of anguish. As soon as I saw you, I was happy and gay. Now when I see you dead, I am overwhelmed with pain. It weighs upon me that my own end is so slow in coming.

"Noblemen of Rome, for the love of God, take pity! Help me to lament the loss of my loved one. Great is this sorrow which has fallen upon me. I cannot do enough so that my heart has its fill. Does that surprise you? I have no longer either daughter or son."

Between the grief of the father and the mother came the maiden whom he had wed. "Sire," said she, "how long has been the wait that I have waited in the house of your father where you left me sorrowing and bewildered.... Sir Alexis, I have missed you for so many days, and wept so many tears for this body of yours, and so many times have looked for you from far away . . . to see if you would return to comfort your wife, . . . I did these things not at all out of treachery, or from fatigue. Oh, dear love, how lovely were you in youth! It hurts me to think that it will rot in earth. Oh! gentle man, how sorrowful I can be! I was waiting for good news from you, but I see now that the news is bitter and evil!

"Oh, beautiful lips, beautiful face, beautiful manner, . . . how your beautiful body has changed! I loved you more than any living creature. What great sorrow has loomed before me! It would have been better for me, love, if I had been dead. . . . If I had known you were there at the bottom of the steps, there where you lay stretched out in your long weakness, never anyone could have kept me from staying close together with you. If it had been permitted me, I would have tended you.

"Now I am a widow, sir," said the maiden. "I shall never have any joy, for that cannot be. Never in all the world will I ever have a man. I will serve God the King who rules over all. He will not fail me, if He sees that I serve Him."

The father and the mother and the maiden wept so much there that they all were exhausted. During this time all the lords prepared the holy body and laid it out beautifully according to their custom. [How fortunate were those who devoutly ministered to him!]

"Sirs, what are you doing?" said the high prelate. "What does this shrieking and this weeping and this noise signify? Let whoever will do so lament; for us this is a great joy since through this man we shall receive good aid. Thus let us pray that he deliver us from evil."

All those who could come close enough lifted up his body. Singing they bore the body of Saint Alexis. All prayed that he have pity on them. It was unnecessary to notify those who had heard the news. Both great and small came running. Thus the entire populace of Rome was moved. Those who came first were those who ran the fastest. Such great crowds of people came down the streets that neither king nor count could make his passage through them. Nor could they break through the masses of people with the sainted body.

The lords began to confer among themselves. "The throng is so great that we shall never pass through. The people who have missed him so much rush here for the sake of this holy body which God has given us. No one can direct them away from here."

Those who govern the empire reply with these words: "Do not be impatient, sirs, for we shall find a remedy. From our possessions we will make generous distributions to the little people who desire alms. If they crowd about us, then we will be rid of them." From their treasuries they take out gold and silver and have it thrown before the poor people. They think by that to be disencumbered of the crowds, but that cannot be. These people want nothing from them. Their thoughts are bent upon the holy body.

In one voice the little people cry out: "We take no notice

17

of their wealth. Because of this holy body such great joy has appeared before us that we have no concern for any other treasure. If God so pleases, we shall have good assistance from him. . . ." Long ago in Rome there was such great bliss, as there was on that day for poor and for rich because of the holy body which they had in their power. They have the idea that it is God himself whom they are holding. All the people praise God and give Him thanks.

Saint Alexis wished them well, indeed. For that he is today held in honor, even to this day. His body is in the city of Rome, and his soul is in God's paradise. The man who is seated there can well be joyful. He who has sinned can well remember this: he can be saved perfectly well through repentance.

Brief is this age; wait for one more enduring. Let us ask the Holy Trinity that together with God we may reign in heaven. Deaf, nor blind, nor crippled, nor leper, nor mute, nor bruised, nor paralyzed, and especially no sick person, . . . no man among them goes away from him afflicted. Not a single one bears his pain away with him. Not an infirm person ill with any infirmity does not on the spot regain his health by only calling upon his name. Some folks go by themselves. Others have themselves carried there. God showed them His true miracles. Those who came weeping sang as they left his side.

When the two lords who govern the empire see these very visible signs of his healing power, then they receive his body; they lift him up and thus they do him homage. Somewhat by entreaty, and somewhat by force, they push their way through the crowd. Saint Boniface whom we call The Martyr has a very beautiful church in Rome; to it they unhesitatingly carry Saint Alexis and gently lay him on the ground. Happy the place where his holy body reposes!

For seven days the people of Rome, through their own demands, keep him for whom they longed so long, above ground. The throngs are great. No need to inquire about that. They so surrounded him on all sides that one could draw near him only with great difficulty. On the seventh day a final resting place was made for his holy body, for this heavenly gem. Then they retire at a distance. Then the crowds disperse. Whether they wish it or not, they allow him to be lowered into the ground. This grieves them deeply, but it can hardly be otherwise.

With censors, with golden candelabra, the learned clergy gowned in albs and stoles lay his body in a marble sarcophagus. Most of them are chanting. The greatest part of them are weeping. They are already wishing that they did not have to tear themselves away from him. The coffin was adorned with gold and precious jewels in honor of the holy man whom they must lower down into the ground; and into the ground they drop him by the sheer force of their wills. The people of the city Rome weep. There is no longer under the sky the man who can console them.

There is no use now telling you more concerning the father, the mother, and the wife, and their outcries. Everyone agreed by word aloud that they were to be pitied. All deplored their bereavement so earnestly that in this day alone were shed one hundred thousand teardrops. Neither could they either keep him longer above ground. Whether they consented willingly or not, they too had to let him be buried. They bade farewell to the body of Saint Alexis. They too besought him similarly to take pity on them, to be their advocate at the seat of the Most High Lord.

The people depart. Henceforth the father and the mother and the maiden do not leave each other. They remained together until they returned to God. Their society was fine and honored. Their souls were saved through this holy body.

Without doubt, Saint Alexis is in heaven, together with God, in the company of the angels, with the maiden to whom he was such a stranger on earth. Now he has her with him. Together are their souls. I know not how to express the extent of their bliss.

Oh, God, what a worthy labor and what a good life of service did this holy man fulfill during his mortal days! For now is his soul filled with glory. He has what he desires. There is no more to be said. For especially, and in this fashion, does he look upon the very God.

Alas, wretched people, how blind we all are! For we see that, and that we are all of us fools. We are so laden with our sins that they put utterly out of our minds a life of right. Should we not through this holy man's example rekindle our flames?

Sirs, let us remember this holy man. Let us pray likewise that he deliver us from evil, that in this century of ours he restore to us peace and happiness, and in the other world that he assure us an everlasting glory in the words of Our Lord. To this end let us recite: "Our Father, which art in heaven, . . ."

Amen.

II

THE ROMANCE OF
GIRART DE VIENE

Bertrand de Bar-sur-Aube

THIRTEENTH CENTURY

OULD YOU LIKE me to tell you a good story of very high history and of very great courage? A better one can scarcely be told or heard. Be sure that this is no tale of haughtiness and folly, of treason and cowardice, but of a sweet nobility which Jesus blesses —and of the proudest man who ever was in life.

You have often heard tell of Girart de Viene, whose exploits were so daring. But the storytellers have forgotten or didn't even know those details of his story that I will tell you now—all about Girart and about his father also. So I will tell you as best I can.

A Count Garins had four very daring sons, the most chivalrous that ever were seen. However, despite their proficiency with weapons of war, the five were destitute of wealth and also of lands, as you will see.

It was in the month of May when it is nice and warm, when the green grass grows and the meadows are in bloom. At Bar-sur-Aube sat your author Bertrand, pensively in his garden. This gentle scholar Bertrand, who is telling you this story, heard, upon coming out of church, a burly pilgrim who had adored and served Saint James and who had just returned from Rome. The pilgrim told him this story of the adventures and great trials which Sir Girart suffered before he got Viene.

At the joyous feast of Easter, which the Lord God ordained on earth, old Count Garins was in the ancient city of Monglaive with his household, whom he loved dearly. He had four sons of high birth. They were strapping and daring and full of mettle. But things were so bad that between them there wasn't so much as a crust of bread, nor a scrap of salt meat, nor a single drop of wine. All they had in their possession were four cakes and two peacocks in the vaulted hall of Monglaive. The Count had also one war horse, one Syrian mule, four coins, and three lances. The father realized this, and his heart was so touched that be began to cry. He was desolate. The tears dripped on his white beard.

Hernaut saw this. His blood boiled so that he could not keep from saying harshly, "What's the trouble with you, father? By God the son of Mary, I see you crying. That looks foolish. Tell me. Are you hiding something from me? Either I must know it, or by God the son of Mary, I shall never have joy in my whole life. It is treason."

The gallant Hernaut then added, "Sir father, may God (who established our laws) help me, but I see you crying. I am upset. If you don't tell me why, my heart will be distressed. This sorrow, I think, will split me in three."

"Sons," said the father, "I will tell it to you rather. So help

me God, who is our Sovereign Lord, it is for you that I am in such a state. When I see you dressed in plain gray cloth, you seem just ordinary burghers to me—of low estate and of poor equipment. Do you think, children, that I would not be distressed by the poverty you are suffering against my will? The heathen Emir exiled us from our castles and our manors and holds our lands so tightly that we can't get a coin from them. It is most shameful that we don't have food for more than two or three days. I have fear of my life."

The wise Hernaut said, "Good father, it is a great shame to lose your wits in this way. There is no man under the sky whom his relatives will not consider more vile if he becomes dismayed. On the other hand, I will say what seems right to me. Such a man as goes groaning along will never make it to Saint John's Day, will never have a castle or a city or a burg or a town to call his own—nor ermine, nor gray, nor spotted fur. . . . It is Easter time and a joyous day when both little and great are carefree and glad. Therefore joyfully give us some food; for you don't know, father, whether you will be able to do that much longer."

The father called for food and water, and they all sat down. There wasn't a great plenty. When they had eaten, the boys went out to play. Hernaut rode the horse because he was the most intelligent. The other three went skipping along on foot. Since they had not yet been dubbed knights, they could only take bows and arrows. Out the castle portal they went on their quest. Beyond its walls ran the murmuring Rhone. It is a marvelous and great river which brought them ships and barges.

Girart looked ahead of him down the highway. There against the setting sun he saw between three hills and a green wood eight heathen pagans leading twenty heavily loaded mules. Girart called his brothers. "Sirs," he said, "hear what I think. I see some Saracen merchants coming

24

up from Spain with twenty mules heavily loaded with goods."

Then the youngest brother Girart called to his brother Rainier. "Sir," he said, "I do not wish to conceal anything. I see twenty pack animals loaded with silver and refined gold. My father Garins has great need of them, for he and my lady have hardly anything left to eat. Today I saw my father weep and cry. Henceforth we ought to help him by conquest and by our earnings."

Hernaut answered, "Let them approach. Then by the cross which palmers seek, truly I would be the first to send the steel arrow through their bodies." And so he did. Then the brothers seized the mules, killed those attendants who had not run away, and took the booty home to their father. Then they were all rich and powerful.

On the Wednesday after Easter the four brothers came out of chapel. They had already made their decision. "Father," said Hernaut, "you live here among unbelievers, but your city is so strong that it does not need to fear any assault, for which I thank God who made the sky and the dew. We have brought you such wealth and conquered so many pagans that you and your vassals have enough food for a year. Therefore, father, with your consent we will go forth to make our fortunes in a strange land."

"By God," said the second son Mile, "I wish to go to Rome without delay and pray Saint Peter that he give me the honor I have desired so much." (It was Mile who later became the Duke of Salerno.)

Hernaut went to the large city of Biaulande where he married a beautiful wife and inherited his uncle's fief. He became the father of the celebrated Aimeri de Narbonne. . . . Now, here begins our story.

Neither Rainier nor Girart asked for either a servant or a groom. Each one rode an ambling mule. They passed along many a hill, many dark forest paths, many deep woods, and many swift torrents until they came to Viene. They stopped that night at the home of a rich bourgeois named Hermin who lived beside the Rhone. After a good dinner of wine, venison, and mulled wine, they took a walk through the city. Girart saw Viene with its high walls of marble. "Look at this well-seated city," he said to his brother. "I never saw such a noble one in my whole life. There isn't a better one in this worthy century."

The following day they traveled as far as Cluny where they were guests of the Abbot Morant. "Where are you from, children?" he asked. "From what lineage?"

"I am Rainier, the son of Garins of Monglaive, from a powerful city in Gascony. We are going into France to serve King Charles."

"You are of high lineage," said the Abbot. "Were you never dubbed?"

"No, sir," answered Rainier. "Because of his dire poverty, we have been cast adrift in the world by our father who sired us."

The Abbot then ordered that rich garments be given to the boys. Girart was overjoyed. "God," he said, "Father of Majesty, look how rich and well provided we are! Thank God and Saint Peter! I will return it to you, everything you have given me, if I live to be a man."

Without stopping long in Burgundy, they continued up to Paris. To their disappointment King Charles was in Rheims. They therefore rode on until they arrived in Rheims where they heard that poverty was considered very vile. For eight full days they remained in Rheims without being able to see the king. Nor were they invited to eat or drink at court. Finally on the eighth day Girart told his brother: "Sir, what is your thought? We have stayed here for eight days without having spoken to Charlemagne and without having gone to his court. We have received neither oats for our mules nor a coin for ourselves. Yet we are still here. We won't get a peeled egg, nor any clothes, nor a saddled mule. The clever devil brought us here. This country is full of scarcity. We were better off at home where we were born. Let's go. We have been here too long."

"If I go away," replied Rainier, "may my body be damned! When we return to Monglaive, our powerful relatives will ask us where we have been. I will say in the city of Paris and then in Rheims where we found the king. And if I have never seen him nor looked at him, have never had oats or money from him, they will consider me a tamed quitter. And I would be ridiculed and jeered at. Therefore I *shall* go to the court. I *shall* get grain, or they will pay for it dearly before I depart."

Girart and Rainier went to court with their petition. They passed through the outer gates despite the porter. They asked for water. They sat down to eat. . . . All they were served was a small roll—and once to drink! That was a poor meal. As they saw it, the only thing to do was to fly into a rage. The seneschal began to address the room. The boys studied him.

He wore a very expensive ermine and an embroidered gown which he had had made for himself. A newly dubbed knight had made him this present. He held in his hand an applewood staff. In a haughty and arrogant voice he began to bawl: "Now come for your oats, squires! But by the cross which palmers seek, if you get me irritated, you won't get any, by God the Just."

"Give me some, sir," said Rainier. "My mule had nothing to eat last night. God help me, but you sin if you do not consent either to see or to receive us. If you need our services, take them freely and of our accord."

The rogues present saw the boys were from another country. They looked them up and down and concluded they weren't worth a straw. Most haughtily they began to revile them. "Stay down, shepherds, sons of whores, you foreigners, Bedouins, tricksters. There isn't a ribald nor a trotting groom who doesn't ask for oats for his pack ass. I doubt if he owns a horse. Let him have fodder when we want to give him some. Let him go back and pay his innkeeper for his bed and lodging, if he can."

The seneschal raised his staff to strike Rainier, and he also began to upbraid him. "Whoreson, low fellow, woolcarder! You thought wrong when you came for oats at my granary!"

In a white anger Rainier replied, "Whoreson also, traitor, coward!" He grabbed him so hard that he made him stagger. He raised his fist and struck him so hard full in the mouth that he broke his neck and made him fall to the floor. Then he kicked his body into the loft. "Hey, glutton," he cried. "God should be annoyed with you! You don't know how to dole out provender." Then Rainier began to yell to the others, "Step forward, whoever needs food! Whoever wants a peck can have a bushel!"

Girart measured out grain to all who approached. Every mule in town had plenty to chew on that night! Girart carried a bushelful home to his mount. As the brothers swaggered their way out of the court, they sent squires and servants flying.... One sirrah ran to announce this news to the king. "On my oath, Sire," he said, "we have had some trouble. A squire has killed the seneschal, who sprawls in the loft. I think he broke his neck. I saw blood spurt out of his mouth. If you don't get revenge, you won't be worth a straw."

Charlemagne had no alternative but to become angry. He summoned two of his officers. "Have the doors bolted and barred. Early tomorrow have the hostelries searched. Let no squire, however important he may be, escape without paying through the nose for this. I'll have the culprit's ears cut off, his eyes put out, and his nose shortened."

Some nobody answered, "A good decision."

Rainier returned to his hostelry where he had plenty of

figs and dainties to eat that night. The brothers lived well
for once. (I suppose, Lord Barons, you have heard enough
times that no sooner is a man dead and gone to his end
than he is a thing put out of mind.)

On the following morning, as soon as it was daylight, the
high-born brothers got up, put on their shoes and their
clothes, and Rainier called his brother. "Let's go to court,
brother," he said. "We've been here too long. We will go
find out what has been said and done."

"Upon my word," replied Girart, "I dread that oaf who
was laid out in the loft yesterday. If he is dead, we are in
trouble. I have an idea we will be blamed. We are likely not
to have a friend in this whole country."

"Don't chafe about it," Rainier told him. "The king has
plenty of boys in attendance. If he loses one, he can get
thirteen others."

The brothers were commendable. Without delay they
marched up to court where the Emperor was hearing mass
in the chapel. The chapel door was bolted. There was such
a crowd of courtiers massed outside that the brothers
couldn't come or go. Rainier shoved his way up to the
barred door. He gave it such a boot with his foot that it
cracked and burst inwards. Seeing this, the bailiff lifted his
staff to strike Rainier. He hit him, in fact, such a blow that
it raised a lump on Rainier's head. "Whoreson" said the
officer, "outlander, get out of here! How dare you think you
can kick in the king's door! Can't you see these high and
praiseworthy lords, clad in gray silk from the Holy Land,
who can't even enter themselves? And you think that you, who
have only a gray homespun to your back, can come inside?"

Then the gently born Rainier answered, "Whoreson, evil
and stubborn glutton, may God damn you! My heart is not
made of ermine or astrakhan. It is in my belly where God
placed it. That man is rich who has a stout heart. That man
is poor who is proud and insolent. I'd be cut up in chunks

rather than look and act like you." Then he kicked the door into two pieces and hit the officer so hard in the face that one of his eyes flew out and landed on the broken door.

Hearing the noise, Charlemagne of the proud countenance left the service to ask who had broken his door and killed his doorman.

"I did it, Sire," answered Rainier. "May God have the soul of this oaf who struck me first with his stick. But, thank God, I am well revenged. Honorable Emperor, before God the Just, I could testify in any court of emperor or king or prince that when one sees a poor man and a stranger, a gentle man will greet him—not beat him or manhandle him—for such is a poor man whose courage is proud, and such was the powerful man whose heart was rotten. Just Sire, I do not seek to deny it—he should in all reason have permitted me to explain my errand. If he had known who I am and what I want, he would have had no reason to touch me."

"Truly spoken," said the courtiers. "Pardon him, Sire."

"Who are you, Sir Child?" asked Charlemagne. When he heard their story, he dismissed them with a present of money.

"Go!" Rainier told Girart. "Saddle my ambling mule. I have no desire for his money. I am not a tradesman. If I had this whole palace full of money, I wouldn't keep any of it. Let soldiers, sergeants, priests, monks, and other poor folks scramble for money! I'll never be a burgher or a merchant in my entire life. I see this king who goes refusing our services. Let us look for another lord who will do us more honor and give us a higher standing."

"How courtly and wise are these children," commented the other French lords.

"Just Sire," said one. "Retain them for they are noble and valiant. They offer you their services and will do your commands."

Then said the king, "Well, let them come forward and become my men. First I will dub Rainier and make Girart my squire."

Rainier performed so many great feats of arms that Charlemagne did not regret his decision. One day at Pentecost time when Charlemagne was holding his court at Paris, he summoned all his nobles to attend. The king wished to celebrate the feast day in high style. He commanded Girart and Rainier to serve him at dinner, and they did not wish to refuse. One of them presented each dish to the emperor, and the other held the large goblet of shining gold which was full of spiced wine. They were attending upon the royal table when a messenger arrived.

"God save Charlemagne," said the messenger, "and all his high lords whom I see beside him. . . . Show me proud Girart and the Rainier whom Charlemagne dubbed a knight."

"Look here, then," replied Rainier of the proud face. "What do you want to ask me? Do you have news of our friends?"

"Yes, Sire, know that I do. Mile is in Apulia, governing all that land. He has two sons of whom he can rightfully be proud. Hernaut has a son and is the king of his country. What can I tell them about you? Have you lands and castles of your own to guard?"

"Such a thing," replied Rainier, "is not to be asked. Tell them for me that we serve the great Charlemagne. My brother Girart helps prepare the food in the kitchen. He also washes the pots and pans and dries them. I do the laundry and take charge of the linen closets. From time to time the king lets us run in the pasture like the other jades. We serve him, in other words."

"Are you telling me the truth?" asked the messenger. "Have you really no lands or county or city of your own?"

"You're asking foolishness," scoffed Rainier, "My brother

Girart doesn't even know what chivalry is. You never saw a person like him in all your life. . . . I keep the linen; that is my domain. But, as I swear before God, if Charles King of France does not give me land and estates, I shall never serve him another day of my life. I will go seek another lord."

Charlemagne was leaning on his elbow at the table all this time. He called one of his attendants. "Did you hear what Rainier told this messenger whom you see? . . . The gallows is the only way to redeem a rogue. . . . These here are of vile birth."

When Rainier heard these words, he changed color. "What city have you given us, what lands, what fiefs, or what county? You dubbed me. That's a proven fact. But I have had no other rewards for all the territories I won since that time in your name. Tomorrow I shall go home to Monglaive."

"Vassal," replied Charlemagne, "you became my man and carried my standard into battle. You won many engagements. You also bragged in front of countless barons that you would rule—whether I wished it or not—over Frenchman, Burgundian, German, Flemish, and Frisian. This you did like a rogue."

"Mercy, frank King," said Girart. "If you please, we will leave immediately, naked and unprovided, a staff in our hands. Thus wandering, we will return home."

"On my head," swore Rainier, "we will not!"

Then the emperor became exceedingly angry. "Did you hear what these boys said?" he asked his lords. "By the Apostles, if they are still here three days from now, I will have them strung up to a tree!"

Then Rainier said, "Don't you remember that day, some time ago, when I saw you fall from your horse onto the ground? It was in a grassy meadow. I gave you my long-maned war horse while I stood there on foot. Then I fought so hard that I won me another horse. Before I leave

France, those who now stand silent here may want to say whether or not I lost my pains."

"Charles, dear King," said the gentle Girart, "for the love of God who suffered on the cross, my brother Rainier has such a bad temper. But he is a brave and honorable knight. There isn't in all the land another one like him. For God's sake, keep him in your service. I will be your slave and his bond. I will wait upon you willingly, day after day . . . as long as I live." Girart knelt before the emperor.

Rainier lifted his brother up by the coat, raised his hand, and slapped him across the face. "Stupid, baseborn, ignoble," cried Rainier. "I would rather be cut up and killed than to have you so bonded and enslaved. That would ruin our family forever. If King Charlemagne does not give me land today, I will never again be his man as long as I live. I'll go home to my father."

Then a lord named Henri came to Rainier's defense, reminding the emperor of all the lands this Gascon had won and suggesting that he could be given Genvres-on-the-Sea. The former duke had died two months before. He had left a lovely daughter and no son. After discussion and much persuasion, Rainier and the emperor were reconciled. Genvres was settled upon Rainier, who left immediately with a party of knights to take possession of his new domains. He married the former duke's beautiful daughter and became the father of Roland's friend Olivier and of the lovely Aude who was Roland's affianced bride. . . . (That was a wedding God did not allow to come to pass! . . .) Girart remained at the court of Charlemagne where he was highly praised and deeply loved by the barons and peers of the realm.

One day Charlemagne organized a great hunt. His huntsmen came. The dogs were unleashed with hue and cry. They took two stags and a wild boar. Around noon, when they were about ready to leave the forest, a great storm burst. It began to rain and to thunder. The king sought shelter under an oak tree. Suddenly a messenger from Burgundy appeared. "I have news for you, Sire," he said, after having greeted the king. "The lordly Duke of Burgundy has just died, and the duchess wishes to speak to you. Please set a time and place where she can find you."

"I shall decide it now," replied Charlemagne. "She will find me at Sens on Saint John's Day." After the messenger had withdrawn, the king sat deep in thought. Then he recalled the Duke of Burgundy. He wept for him. He knew, however, that his weeping would recover nothing. He looked up to see Girart there before him. It occurred to Charlemagne to give both the lady and the duchy to Girart.... Within the next few days he dubbed Girart a knight, making him also a very rich gift of horses and armor. . . . Girart was overcome with gratitude. He paid all homage to the King.... (That respect did him very little good, as you will see.)

At this feast of Saint John, where there is always a great celebration, the powerful King of France journeyed to Sens where the Duchess of Burgundy awaited him. Two archbishops were also present. When the king saw the lady, he exclaimed in a loud voice, "Frank Duchess, be thee well come!"

"God, the Father most powerful, keep you, Sire," she said.

"Lady, you have had a great loss in this very great duke whom you loved so much."

"Sire, it weighs heavily upon me, but mourning does not recover the loss. If you please, I request another husband; for it is the custom since the time of Moses that when one dies, another fills his place. After a dead one I need one living because my domains have dire need of a master. Without one, I stand to lose too much."

"Lady," he replied, "well I believe it. I have a virgin

34

knight here, and a very handsome lad. His name is Girart. He is courteous and promising, proud and daring, and of very keen intelligence. He is son to Garins of Monglaive, a valiant baron from a city in greater Gascony."

"Sire," she said, "let it be as God ordains. My only desire is to accede to your commands, for I am your liege subject."

While they were conversing, the emperor looked closely at the lady. He saw that she was beautiful and cultured and gracious. Her eyes were green. Her cheeks were pink, and her skin was whiter than snow upon frost. "God," said the king to himself. "Sainted Virgin whom I honor, I don't find in this whole country a single woman who pleases and charms me. Now this one is so beautiful and so gracious that a prettier one could certainly not be found. By that Lord who made the sky and the dew, this is the one that I shall have to wife. Girart can get himself a wife in some other country."

As soon as Charlemagne said it, then it was a fact. So he called for a great tournament—where many a brave soul was severed from many a body—and a round of festivities. King Charles did not delay many days. He summoned the Duchess into his council. "Lady," he said, "let us not hide our object. If it pleases you and so makes you happy, I will have you for my married woman."

When the lady heard him, she sat deep in thought for some time. Then she replied, "Sire, you were apparently playing with me a few days ago. . . . No king ought to select as his wife a vavasor from his own country. That's a well established fact. Only the daughter of a king should be given to you, or some other lady of very great fame. . . . Just give me Girart of the alert face. . . . I was presented to him first. If I were to refuse him now, I would be severely blamed. . . . Great Sire, let us not dissemble: I will not be your queen."

"What I hear is silly," the emperor replied. "My Lady

Duchess, you actually deserve to be blamed. You are not quick-witted. I won't try to keep that fact from you. Which is better, to rise or to fall? Which do you prefer, to extinguish your family or to raise it up?"

"Sire," she said, "don't fool about with me like this. You could marry in the highest rank—the daughter of a king or a duke or a peer. And you should reflect before you even consider such an alliance with me. Give me Girart whom I have heard praised. He is handsome. He is young. He is a courteous knight bachelor. If you give him to me, I do not desire to refuse him. If I were to refuse, I should be very blameworthy. . . .

"If you please, Sire, I beg leave to withdraw now. I must discuss this matter with my advisers and ask for their opinions as to whether I shall take you or Don Girart the knight."

"Lady," he said, "I shall grant your leave willingly. He who seeks counsel usually derives great good from it."

The lady requested the four counts who had escorted her to convene at her *hôtel*. Girart sent word to her asking to be received. And permission was granted at once. Girart was wearing in the lady's honor a pale, shiny ermine cloak and a silken robe from the Holy Land. He rode a mule which had a fine saddle, as rich as any that could be found. The bridle alone was worth 100 pounds of silver. Along the streets rode Girart. All along the way people pointed to him and said: "Look at Girart, the valiant knight bachelor. He who serves a noble man like him should make his fortune."

Girart rode up to the lady's *hôtel* without any hindrance. He dismounted before the flight of steps and was about to climb them when he saw that the lady had come out to welcome him. She began to address him most nobly. "Be thee welcome, most gentle and most valorous knight. So help me God, I had to send for you. And so you come,

36

you to whom I owe my love. I do not attempt to conceal my heart from you. I went to the palace to speak to the king. There I heard him ask such a thing as you could never grant nor agree to grant. Sir Girart, I do not wish to hide this from you. Take me for your wife, if you wish to consent to my request. I have no desire to live through a long dispute in this matter. In any case, I never yet saw a quarrel well begun where there were not eventually several people worthy of blame."

"Lady," answered Girart, "I have heard marvelous news! I can most certainly say and take an oath that this is true. Our age begins to be a dreadful one when women go asking men to marry them! On the faith I owe to God, who has us all to save from perdition, from this day onward two years shall pass before I am seen marrying either you or anyone else. So, hunt for another husband—if you can find one. You will never have me, and I tell you that to your face. Do you doubt me!"

The lady listened to what he said. She thought he had gone mad. She never before was so ashamed.

Girart went away without waiting to hear any more. He neither asked nor received her leave to withdraw. He left the duchess in a state of great anger. All that night she neither ate nor drank; all that night she neither lay down nor slept. She waited for dawn. Then she dressed and adorned her person. She went to Saint Stephen's minster where she knelt before the altar. She prayed the Lord God who created the world to give her Girart who had scorned her yesterday. She would love him more than she could ever love the king. After she had prayed, she returned to her *hôtel*. She then sent a servant to Girart to ask him to come to her. He was still so proud, however, that he disdained her summons, asking for fifteen days' respite. When the lady heard this reply, she almost went out of her mind.

Over and over she turned the matter in her mind, wondering if she had a move left or if the game were lost. If she didn't get a new duke, then the king would take her. . . . Then the emperor sent for her to come at once, but in the meantime he went to her. When she greeted him, he bowed very beautifully before her. "Sire," she said, "I shall conceal this from you no longer. . . . I am very glad that you have come. . . ."

Charles the King of the worthy Kingdom of France walked across the tiled floor where he had found the Duchess of Burgundy. The two of them spoke privately to each other. The king paid his respects most courteously to the lady, who very sensibly returned his compliments. "Sire," she said, "please hear my thoughts. My desires should not be concealed from you. True it is that when you summoned me yesterday, I took no time to think clearly. Since that hour I have pondered certain matters which came later to my memory. That's a holy truth. I also thought about your own reasons as you explained them to me. My personal household officers praise me sincerely, and I want you to know I have quite made up my mind. I would rather be crowned Queen of the worthy Kingdom of France for fifteen days than be proclaimed a duchess for fourteen years!"

When the king heard this, he was delighted. He summoned the lords who had accompanied him. "Sirs," he said, "there is no need to conceal this news. Look upon this lady whom you have so praised to me. I shall take her to be my married woman."

Then Girart said, "You gave her to me, plus all her land and all her estates!"

She answered (she had a good tongue in her head), "By the very faith I have in God, I would rather be dragged by wild horses, drowned in water, or burned in the fire, than ever have private knowledge of your body. It is proven truth on this very day that Charlemagne gave me to you the other day and that you refused me. I am still very much humilitated because of it."

Then our emperor so treated her that everyone saw his great esteem. He gave his right hand to this courteous woman. Then he began to address his knights. "See before you this lady of the proud countenance. I would take her, if you will consent to grant it."

Girart then said, "Sire, honorable King, you do me great injury, and I do not wish to hide that fact. For you gave me this lady the other yesterday and made me lord of all her lands. You are my liege lord. I cannot receive my due ahead of you."

Even so, the king did not wish to let her go for this. He had her escorted into the minster and wedded to him there by the archbishop. The wedding party then returned to the palace, which was full to overflowing. The celebration and merriment lasted all that day. (I can't begin to describe all the rich dishes that were served. There were so many that I wouldn't know how to list them.)

At vespers when the king's duty was to go to bed, two archbishops came to bless the wedding chamber. Several noble knights waited upon the king. "Girart, the brave warrior, is very much angered. Settle upon him lands and honors in perpetuity. Let not anyone be able to spread such an ugly story: that you have scorned your own knight."

The king replied ,"I agree to make such restitution. For the love of you and for your pleas, and also for Girart for whom I have a real affection, I give him Viene and its title. High are its walls and its moat wide and deep. Rich is this city and much to be dreaded. He will have ample to eat and to drink. His enemies will besiege him in vain. He can come to my aid also if the need ever arises."

The attendant lords hailed this announcement. "Great is this gift, Girart, brave knight! Now you must thank the emperor!"

"In the name of God, willingly!" said Girart.

In the emperor's chamber where he had retired in order to go to bed, attendants banked down the fire for the night. The knight Girart went straight up to his king and knelt beside the bed, to embrace his leg as a sign of his gratitude. . . . It was not the emperor, however, whose leg was extended from under the bed covers. But the duchess, because of her great wrath, stretched out her foot, and thus caused him to kiss it. . . . (The devil, no doubt, wanted to ensnare her in his toils as soon as she was naked.)

This act of hers caused a long dissension to disturb the realm. If the gentle knight had only known it, he would have pierced her with his steel dagger, he who stooped so low as to kiss her foot! (Such mortal wars arose because of it that she should have been cut down then and there!)

Then Duke Girart had Viene, that very ancient city which the king bestowed upon him of beloved memory. But Duke Girart did not know the whole proven truth, how this thing had happened, and about the duchess, so unbalanced and so foolish, who had done such a thing in the tiled state chamber. Very dearly, indeed, was this insult repaid. Even she became frantic because of what she had done.

However, when the king had married the lady and had had her called queen throughout the kingdom of France, early that morning as soon as it was daybreak, Duke Girart delayed no longer. After he had heard mass, he requested leave to depart. The king bestowed a fine train of attendants upon him and gave him great wealth to carry away. Duke Girart traveled all that day . . . and the day after, until he came again to the monastery of Cluny where he spent the night.

"Do you know me?" he asked the abbot.

"To tell you the truth, I don't," replied the abbot. "I never saw you before in my life."

"You once made me rich gifts, sir, of robes and clothes. I

40

have not forgotten it. I therefore repay my debt to you now."

After several days of traveling, Duke Girart arrived at Viene where he took possession of his duchy. That very year he took a wife whose name was Guiborc, the sister of King Otto. Two sons were born of this union, Savari and Otto.

Years later Duke Girart was visited by his nephew Aymeri, son of Hernaut. After having seen Viene and become acquainted with his uncle, the young Aymeri decided to visit Charlemagne's court. Duke Girart outfitted him handsomely and gave him two attendants. On the way to Paris Aymeri was able to kill several brigands who had been infesting the forests. He arrived at court one evening in time for supper. Aymeri was not at all shy. He seated himself, ate a hearty supper, and then presented his respects to the king.

"Friend," replied Charlemagne, "may God grant you an increase of goodness. Where are you from, or where are you bound? From what land are you or where born? How are you named? Take care not to conceal it."

"Sire," he said, "my name is Aymeri. I am son to Hernaut of Biaulande."

Then the queen said, "What a handsome lad he is! I never saw one from Auvergne who was so courtly. Usually men from there are treacherous fellows and liars for sure. Take, for example, Sir Girart of Viene. I wouldn't give a straw for him."

Then Aymeri turned to the lady. "I am the son of Hernaut and the nephew of Girart, whose courage is so proven.

I pray you before God not to slander him in the least, for—
so help me God—I would be very grieved."

After this conversation Charlemagne was informed by a
monk how Aymeri had rid the forest of robbers. The king
was so pleased that he promised to dub Aymeri a knight
within fifteen days. Then he adjourned his court and escorted the queen to Saint-Denis. Aymeri accompanied them.

One evening as they were dining, the queen began again
to converse with Aymeri. "Now listen, brave and gentle
knight, for I shall tell you something that I never before
revealed. Duke Auberis of Burgundy died leaving me a
widow alone to maintain order in the duchy. I came here to
Charles, this King of Saint-Denis, to ask for and to demand
another husband. He gave me Sir Girart of the marches. I
summoned that knight to hear his opinion. He never came
—which made me feel as if he considered me of small
estate. Then he requested a delay of fifteen days. . . . When
I summoned Charlemagne, however, he of the proud
countenance came willingly at my request—and not unwill-
ingly. I thank God that he married me according to the
advice of his peers.

"After our wedding supper—when it was dark—the king
showed his gratitude by bestowing the city of Viene and
all its lands upon Girart. The king lay beside me in the
bed. Sir Girart knelt down to thank Charlemagne. As it
seemed to me, he was about to kiss the king's leg. In front of
the king I put my leg so that it protruded from the gray
blanket. I had Sir Girart kiss my naked leg with his naked
lips, and I swear that this is the truth. No man of woman
born ever heard this before now!

"This vengeance was well taken on one so haughty. If he
made a fool of me, I humiliated him. I was very well
revenged."

Aymeri was a brave youth. When the queen had finished
her story of outrage and bragging and self-love, Aymeri

42

thought he would explode from anger. He ate no more. He couldn't even cut his meat. He leaped to his feet. He was all anger. From rage he began to yell, "If you did this thing which I have just heard you say, then it was the work of a whore; and I won't hide that opinion. Sir Girart is a valiant warrior. I will die of grief if I cannot avenge him."

He held a knife in his hand. The blade was of steel. Looking down at those who were eating, he raised his hand to throw the knife. Quickly she threw herself back on her cushions. Aymeri's knife landed in a wooden pillar beside her. Then Aymeri leaped forward towards her between the rows of lords. If they had not arisen and caught him, he would have killed her. They surrounded him from in front and behind. The catastrophe was averted by only a second.

"Friends," said Aymeri to his attendants, "it is dangerous to remain longer in this country. God confound me if I care to stay here! Let's to Viene!"

After Aymeri had left the hall, the French lords said to the queen, "God above, what an evil tale was told by a woman! Lady Queen, evil has come to us now! Why did you say it? He never knew it before—nor did we. If that knife had gone through your ladyship instead of landing on the wooden column, your private conversation would have cost you very dear."

"Sirs," she said, "I have been so frightened that I shall not recover my health for a month."

Aymeri did not delay on the way to Viene. He took the same road back and traveled so hastily that he arrived there one evening. He was so angry that when his uncle asked about his trip to France, whether or not he had seen the king, and if he had won rich gifts, Aymeri could not even speak at first. Finally he began his story.

"By God, good uncle, evil has fallen upon us. Never again shall I go into France for love of that queen! . . . I have bad news to announce. You were unfortunate when you paid court to Charlemagne. The queen desires to revile us, to shame our house and to debase us. When Charlemagne took that woman to wife, at night after vespers when he went to bed, his peers advised him to give us Viene. You went to his feet to thank him. And the queen out of hatred extended her foot and thus made you kiss it. Right there at Saint-Denis the other yesterday she bragged of it in front of many knights. I was going to kill her with a great steel blade when the barons booted me out."

Girart heard him. He thought his blood would change. "By Saint Maurice whom I love," he cried, "so I can be proud of my great estate! I shall go into France with an army behind me and not leave a castle stone upon stone, nor a burg, nor a city, nor a minster standing."

Aymeri said, "By God the Just, if you do what I have just heard you pledge, you can take me on as your man. My uncle Rainier will help you also. So will my father Hernaut of Biaulande and so will my uncle Mile.

"Let us go tell Rainier," said Girart.

When Rainier heard the story, he grew red in the face. "Her whoredom will be bought dearly," swore Rainier. "Let France be destroyed and laid waste. And let the land be reduced to great shame if this woman is not released and delivered to us and absolutely abandoned to our vengeance."

An army assembled at Viene. Hernaut arrived with a thousand knights. Mile arrived with his knights. Their father Garins came with seven thousand men. He was the handsomest man from Viene to Montpellier. After the four brothers and their father had been welcomed and made comfortable, Aymeri told them all the story of Charlemagne, the queen, Sir Girart, and the kiss. "Let us to war," said Garins. "Let us make it horrible and heavy! Let us all ride against Charlemagne!"

Messengers from the king arrived to summon Duke Girart into his presence. The brothers and Aymeri found the king at Châlons. "Welcome, knights," said the king. "I am grateful to you for having come to me."

"You have deserved it ill," retorted Hernaut. "Accursed is he who is a friend to you."

The king was astounded by that reply. Then he noticed Aymeri. "Welcome, gentle youth! I saw you not long ago at Saint-Denis."

"I had so many blows there that I won't soon forget it," replied Aymeri. "And the queen beat my ears with such a tale that I thought I would die."

The emperor heard what he said. Beside him sat the queen, very much abashed. He looked at her and then summoned Girart. "Sir," he said, "do not hide anything from me. Are all these people yours? Who is the one with the flowering beard?"

"Just Emperor, this is my father whom Jesus blesses. These are my brothers. Sire, while I ask it, grant me redress for the great stupidity which the queen through foolishness bragged of in the chamber."

The king heard him. He burst out laughing. In a loud voice he called his seneschal. "Go inquire if it is true or untrue," he said. "If true, I will attend to it more closely than any man alive. If it is not true, I will not permit it to be talked about further."

"Sir Girart," said the wise Duke Naimes, "accept a liberal compensation."

"That is no offer," replied Girart. "If I were to be given Milan, Rome, Pavia, and Toulouse, I would not settle. And I will not settle until I get a revenge on the queen that satisfies me; but of her exceeding pride she did this shameful thing and now goes about bragging of it. . . . I shall never be finished with this in my lifetime until I have humiliated her."

"Sir Girart," said Duke Naimes, "will you allow as restitution for damages that she carry your saddle on her head for

45

a league and that she go naked in a wool shirt? If that seems reasonable . . ."

"You are speaking of a pardon," said Garins. "We shall never grant truce or pardon until the day she loses her head under her chin."

"What in Hell!" said one of the king's men. "Who is this flowered mustache who right before us says such a lie?"

These insults ended in a free-for-all between the five and Charlemagne's courtiers. Knights were killed and Garins had his beard pulled before order was restored and the five withdrew. (If they had found the queen in the palace, they would have taken their vengeance then; to my knowledge she was in her chamber, however, where she had the chills.)

The five had not gone very far when they met their reinforcements from Viene. After a fierce pitched battle, the five retreated towards home with Charlemagne and his forces following. The main body of the French army set out behind the king. They brought the queen with them.

When the five were safely shut up inside Viene, they decided after deliberation to continue the war. Rainier wanted to depose Charlemagne and crown Aymeri King of France. The brother Mile disagreed. He felt that Charlemagne was a great king whose death would be a loss to the Christian world.

Charlemagne heard how the brothers had captured one of his cities in Burgundy, and how they were raising an army in the Toulouse area, saying that they would never lay down their arms until he had delivered the queen to them for punishment. Therefore the king sent for warriors from France, promising to dub them and arm them himself. In particular he sent for a great warrior, his nephew Roland. The French knights swore with the king on the reliquary of Saint Simon that they would besiege Viene and that they would remain before its walls for fourteen years—if it were not taken earlier. . . . Eventually the brothers went home to their own domains, leaving Girart and Aymeri inside Viene.

One day Aymeri made a sortie with a hundred and ten knights. They cut a path into Charlemagne's camp where they killed many French knights. "May he who does not strike now be ashamed before God!" cried Aymeri to rally his men as they were surrounded. From the walls of Viene Girart saw that his nephew was in danger. Girart led a party through the gates to their assistance. They found Charlemagne's tent, which they slashed at with their swords until the ridge-pole collapsed.

The king had been inside the tent. He managed to escape to a neighboring tent where he could be armed. . . . The queen ran out after him. Aymeri saw her. Leaning down from his horse, he grabbed her waist and pulled her towards him. Just as he held her close to his horse, Girart saw them. Never was there a man so joyous! He spurred up to the queen with raised sword.

"Uncle Girart!" cried Aymeri. "For the love of God, don't kill her! We will take her to the tower of Viene. There we will take a slower revenge for our anger."

"Nephew," said Girart, "maybe that would be wiser."

But there in the moment of peril were Roland and the noble Baldwin. Without waiting to be fully armed, they leaped on their horses, grabbed their swords, and dug deep with their golden spurs. They saw that Aymeri had lifted the queen into his saddle. They knew he was heading for the gate of Viene. They realized he would shut the queen up inside those walls which years of siege might not cause to surrender—so wealthy was the city. Therefore they raced after Aymeri and Girart.

Roland caught up with Aymeri. He struck him such a blow on the shield that the steel broke. Aymeri fell to the ground. Then Roland helped the queen climb on a war horse. He escorted her back to the master pavilion. . . . Well did he that day preserve her from death!

Charlemagne pursued the siege of Viene for seven years, or until Girart surrendered and made peace. Afterwards, Charlemagne and Roland departed for Spain . . .

III

THE SWAN KNIGHT

Anonymous

THIRTEENTH CENTURY

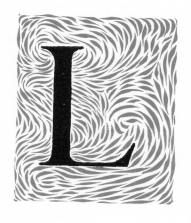

ORDS: Now listen in the name of the Virgin Queen! May Almighty God who distributes all rewards look to receive you too into angelic glory!

And **I** shall sing for you of divine miracles, of monstrous treason, and of a mortal hatred, of arms and of love among personages of noble birth, and of the destruction of the pagan Saracens, of the capture and the wresting of great Jerusalem, of Nicea and Antioch and other distant lands. . . . You will hear of good Duke Godefroy who crossed the "marine" and how he conquered that land of the Muslim god Apollo, how he took Jerusalem which bowed before his crown—not of gold fine enough for his head . . . Jerusalem . . .

Jerusalem where Jesus Christ who sheds light into our lives was crowned upon the cross with a crown of thorns. He wanted no other crown but that poor one. . . .

Lords: Now hear, frank and honorable gentle folk, how I begin this song which is to be recounted, this song of a miracle of ordained truth, this chronicle of absolute truth.

Once upon a time there was a renowned king in the rich city and country of Lillefort. His name was Pietre. He married the Lady Matabrune of Orbendée, married her for the great wealth of her dowry. A marriage so arranged is usually successful; that's proven, unless avarice is the only motive. A love match, as we know, is usually burdensome.

They had a son, whose name was Oriant, who became king of the land and the region after his father's death and under his mother's regency. Oriant was wise, tall, and handsome. Before the young king had even been able to grow a beard, he went hunting with a party of knights into the forest. They gave chase to a great stag which led them deep into the woods. Oriant followed him so closely and so far that he finally found himself all alone under the dark trees. When the stag burst from the covert into a clearing where a little stream ran along a sandy bed, there Oriant lost him. As the king returned homeward, he saw a clear spring of water, a most welcome discovery. He leaped down from his saddle to drink and cool his face. He tethered his horse and sat down, back to a tree, to rest.

As he rested, he saw a wonderfully beautiful maiden, escorted by a knight and two squires and two damsels, ride through the trees. The maiden glimpsed the stranger beside the spring. "Sir," she said, "what are you doing hunting does or deer inside my lands? Have you permission to hunt in my preserves? I saw your stag escape into the stream. If you had killed him, you would have had to pay a fine, whether you liked it or not. I have neither intention nor

inclination to pardon you, for you have no right to hunt or to take venison from my forests."

When Oriant heard her, he raised his chin to look. When he saw that she was beautiful, so pleasing and so intelligent in her words, pleasure, which is the fountainhead of love (which holds all true hearts in subjection), entered into him. After he had looked her up and down closely, Oriant rose to his feet and walked up to her.

"Damsel," he answered gracefully, "I came here beating the bushes under your trees, just as you say; if this land is yours, however, then you hold it from me. You owe me fealty and have paid me homage for it. I am King Oriant, and I swear to it. This forest and all this realm are mine, indeed. Neither one of us is wrong, and as I am guilty of trespassing, then I consent to make honorable amends, particularly since you are so beautiful and so lovely in body, so sweet, so dignified, so pleasant, and so pretty in your manners. May pity and mercy seal us a good bargain, God willing."

The maiden's knight was named Savary. When he recognized the king, he dismounted, knelt at his feet, and said, "I crave your forgiveness for my damsel. She did not recognize you, Sire."

"Knight," said the king, "not so easily done. She owes me amends for her words. I'll forgive her in my bed, and that I do guarantee. It shall be, however, and I speak without hesitation, with her as my wife and I as her husband." Then to the damsel he said, "Sweet maiden endowed with beauty, from this day forward I sue you out of love to become my wife, for you are already my love."

"Sire," the maiden replied, "I would be mad to refuse such company. You are already my lord in high lordliness. If you desire to place me under the sponsorship of one of your knights, then he can remand me to you. I am at your command, whether dead or alive."

Then courteously the king took her hand as he made his oath: "I do swear that while you live I shall never have another wife but you."

The beauty answered: "Dear Sire, I so yield myself to you. I am at your command, whether dead or alive. . . ." Alas! How soon this love was rent!

In the early days of May when the season is joyous, the trees are green, fresh, and flourishing and the sweet night-ingales sing softly, at that time, my lords, Oriant took the maiden with him to the great city of Lillefort. Old Mata-brune went out to meet them. Seeing her, the king said with a laugh, "Lady mother, now walk in joy. I have found the most beautiful girl alive in our century, and a gentle damsel she is and a holder of noble lands. I shall make her my wife, and she has my bond."

"Fine son," said Matabrune, "now do I see you ignorant. You could have had the daughter of King Morghant, and his kingdom with her, and all his vassals."

"Lady," replied the king, "I shall have none of them. I never loved before, not a day of my life. Such a fact and such a state are not very pleasant. The man who has not his pleasure is by that much less valorous. . . . Lady, I want love so much that tomorrow morning I am going to marry her. The thought pleases me so much that I can hardly wait."

"Fine son," said Matabrune, "you can leave all that be. This is no match for you, and make no mistake about it."

The king called for a celebration when it came to supper time. He had the maiden Béatrix honored to the best of his means. All night long he kept the household dancing and caroling. At the point of day he wedded Béatrix. . . . I don't know whether you want me to dwell upon the splendors of the ceremony, the gifts, the musicians, and the dinner. The new queen was lovely and gracious. She let herself be taught by her heart—a much better counselor than anything else.

When it was night, the king went with his queen. That very night also he engendered one daughter and six sons. Next morning the feasting and merriment began all over again.

As soon as the king learned of his wife's pregnancy, he was very happy. One day the queen happened to be leaning at the royal windows when she saw a woman carrying two children to the minster to be baptized. The king, who loved his wife with a perfect and a rare love, was standing beside her at the window. "Sire, on my word," said Queen Béatrix, "I am amazed at what I see."

"At what?" the king asked. "Don't conceal it from me."

"At those two children," she answered briefly, "because I didn't believe, as far as I know, that a woman could conceive two children unless she had carnal relations with two men."

"Lady," he replied, "that's a foolish thing to say. A woman is so organized, by the rights which nature understands in her, that she can have up to seven children from one man perfectly naturally."

Soon after this, King Oriant heard how war was being made upon him. Love for his wife had so besotted him that for six months he had never left her side. Being obliged to lead his knights in person, the king summoned his mother. "Milady, come here," he said. "I must go to war. I leave you my wife, who will give birth very soon. I beseech you for God who restored the world and who arose on the third day from the dead to think of my wife when her time shall have come."

"Fine son," said Matabrune, "I shall think so well of her that she herself will praise me. Go in the name of God who restored the world."

When it was time to leave, the king went to the queen and as a farewell kissed her tenderly. The gentle lady wept pitifully. Her heart hurt her so much that she fainted away from pain. Weeping also, the king lifted her up. Then the two lamented so bitterly that everyone who was present wept to see them.

I won't speak of the war King Oriant fought against a hideous pagan king. Because of you, I don't want to slow up my story. I'll come to the point and so shorten my book. . . . Matabrune (may God punish her!) summoned a matron to whom she said, "Friend, I want to confess to you a thing that must be kept secret. I want you to swear you will hide it. If you will do what I say, I'll give you so much gold and silver that your children can make high marriages." After the woman swore, then Matabrune continued. "You know that my dreaded son has taken an upstart whom I cannot love. I should be delighted, no matter the cost, to see her burn. I want her to be totally dishonored, for she has so bewitched my son that he can neither sleep, nor rest, nor go away from her, nor last unless she is near enough for him to stare and gaze at her body. Now I want to bring the witch to perdition, and I shall tell you without hesitation how we can so befuddle the king that he can re-marry some high lady we will find."

"Lady," said the matron, "I agree to it. I will make the child in her belly as dead as a herring and then tell the king she did it."

"Friend," said the old woman, "do you know what we will do? The queen is so big that we think she has two or three children. I'll tell you how we will go to it. When she goes into labor, we will deliver her children and not show them to her—never show them to her. And then you will tell her that she has had puppies. And then I will take the children and give them to my vassal Marque. We'll put them in water with the fish."

"Lady," said the matron, "it is agreed. I'll go serve the queen with a pleasant face and a false speech."

The night the queen was confined, Matabrune was called and the matron also. The queen had such pain and labored so hard that seven babies came from her side. The pain she felt blinded her heart so that she neither saw nor felt to what she had given birth. And the seven children came splendidly into the world—a daughter and six sons of rare beauty. And each one wore by the will of God a silver chain. This was very dignified. This was a great tribute and high authority. This was a sign of great loyalty and that they were heirs to noble royalty. It was worn and engendered by miracle.

As Matabrune saw the seven little children all wearing silver chains pendant about their necks, then the stupid woman gave them to a chambermaid. Then the evil-thinking matron cried, "Oh, Lady Queen, what great mischief is this! Your bearing is garbage and ill-begotten for from you have tumbled seven stinking dogs, all just now issued from your flanks."

"Now, quick!" said Matabrune, "carry them to the field. Look out that no man alive, lady, nor damsel, knight nor sergeant know it! What a great shame! God save us! Oh, daughter-in-law, how my bones ache! For God's sake confess to us and it is time! Has your body been inhabited by a dog?"

When the lady heard this, her blood ran cold. Her heart went out of her. She couldn't say yes or no. Then they brought her seven puppies they took from a mastiff in the court. They were wrapped in a robe. When the queen regained consciousness, she cried, "Lady, show me my nurslings!"

"To your confusion," said the matron. Then she showed her the pups. The queen wept and wailed.

"Whore," said Matabrune. "You're not worth a button! You are fit to be burned in a coal fire, you who had 'amjunction' with a dog."

"Lady," said the queen. "Leave off such words. I am grief-torn enough without such a lecture."

"The thing can be concealed from your barons," said the matron, "but King Oriant the Lion Heart will have to know it."

"Alas!" the lady cried. "I will never have his pardon. I am not even worthy to have audience with him. When such a desolation has issued from me, I can have no friendship of man or of boy. I am worthy of death by great destruction. If only at least the king would grant me one gift alone —to let me go and stay in religion in a poor abbey where I could remain in prayer. . . ."

Before King Oriant's return, Matabrune called her man Marque. "I want you to do something," she said.

"Say your deed," he answered. "I would not refuse you jewel or boon, nor my hand for treachery or murder, for you raised me in your house and honored my lineage."

"Marque," said Matabrune, "do you know what you will do? I have confidence in you not to betray me and to conceal what I shall ask you do to."

"Lady, you are correct," said that intelligent fellow.

"Then I will tell you my secret. The queen has been confined. She thinks she bore seven puppies instead of seven babies with chains about their necks. Those are signs from God that if they live long, they will become murderers and thieves. So it would be much better to house them in a river, drowned and vanished. So take them and put them where they will be never seen again."

Marque carried the children into the deep woods; but when he saw them laugh, he could not kill them. He kissed them good-bye and abandoned them on a forest path where they were found by a hermit and so saved. A white nanny-goat nursed them. The hermit dressed them in leaves and let them grow up like little wild animals. Meanwhile Matabrune thought they were dead.

King Oriant, after waging a long but successful war, returned home. "Oh, fine son," said Matabrune to him, "how

57

glad is my heart! I am glad to see you return whole and hearty, but I am also sad because of your wife and her pact."

"What, Lady!" he cried. "Is my wife dead?"

"She is dead to you," she said.

"Lady," said the king, "don't spare me. You had better tell me what it is, good or bad, rather than let others come to me first."

"Fine son, my heart is breaking. Your wife's behavior is so bad. I thought that you had engendered a child, but your wife lay with a mutt. She bore seven pups. I was at the delivery and this matron also."

"Where is my wife about whom you go talking?"

"Sire," replied Matabrune, "lying in her chamber. For shame she dares not leave it. She should be burned in a fire on the green meadow."

The king spoke of the matter with one of his trusted knights. He saw that he could neither allow his wife to be burned nor take her to him. The former solution he could not bear, and the second his knights would not allow. Meanwhile the queen despaired and threw herself entirely upon the mercy of Jesus. At the following council of state the king would have been overridden had it not been for the opinion of the Bishop of Lillefort who said:

"The gentle queen bore seven dogs, so they say, for I only know it by report. Let us consider whether she deserves death for this. I say no and for these reasons: her supposed cohabitation must have occurred during her sleep—in any case, against her will. Since you have known her flesh and are bound to her by holy sacrament, you may not consent to her death. Have her carefully guarded in some gracious place. Let vengeance be the Lord's."

After the bishop had spoken, Matabrune grabbed his sleeve and then his chin. "I'll have you die," she told him, "a terrible death."

"Lady," replied the bishop, who had the heart of a lion,

"I believe that if someone heard your confession, the queen would receive her husband's forgiveness."

King Oriant decreed that the queen be kept in solitary confinement. Poor Béatrix, who had expected to be brought at any second to the fire, was overjoyed. Then the king swore before his court that he would never remarry. Because of this oath Matabrune continued to slander the queen and to show the king false evidence of his wife's continued relations with sorcery, the devil, and black magic.

Meanwhile all went well in the forest for the hermit and the seven children he had found. They grew like jackrabbits. Clad in leaves and free, they ran and played and were happy. The hermit baptized them with names of his choice. One of the seven stood out before the others. This was a boy whom the recluse named Hélias. He was taller, handsomer, and more apt at his lessons. The hermit preferred him and relied upon this boy.

One day a poacher saw the children running wild through the trees. He could not get close to them, so wary were they; but he did see the silver chains they wore about their necks. He hurried to the old queen's side. "Lady," he said, "I have had a marvelous adventure and encounter. Even Anselot the warrior nor all the knights and princes of King Arthur's court ever had one such. Lady, I found seven children playing in the woods. They are handsome. They all wear silver chains. Neither Gawain nor Perceval ever had such an adventure."

When Savary and the poacher returned to the forest with Matabrune's orders to kill the seven children, they could only catch six of them. Hélias had accompanied the hermit to market that day. As Savary held the squirming and terrified children in his hands, he suddenly was overcome with terror at their noble features. His blood ran cold at the very thought of the evil old woman who desired the death of such lovely children. He and the poacher therefore decided to remove the silver chains, give them to Matabrune, and tell her that the children were dead but that they had lost one of the chains in their haste. . . . Therefore they slipped the silver chains from the children's necks and released their struggling prisoners.

Before their astounded eyes the six children were transformed into six beautiful white swans which flew away gracefully up through the green branches and into the blue sky.

Matabrune gave the six silver chains to a goldsmith who was ordered to melt them down into a silver goblet. When the artisan put the first chain into his smelter, it multiplied until, with the silver from the one chain, he was able to make two goblets such as the queen had ordered. He carefully stored the five chains in a chest, gave Matabrune one goblet, and kept the other chains for himself.

When Hélias and the hermit returned, they found no trace of the children. They were disconsolate. Hélias divided the bread they had bought in town among five swans which swam in a pond near their hermitage. Every day he remained long hours fondling the swans, feeding them, and caring for them. The hermit continued to educate Hélias whom he was training for the priesthood. The years passed. Hélias was sixteen years old. He had become a man, taller and handsomer and kinder than any man the hermit had ever seen. He was such a good pupil that the recluse had even been able to teach Hélias "true Latin."

Hélias would have become a priest and never known of his origin and never been the ancestor of the good Duke Godefroy de Bouillon had not one day the angel of the Lord appeared to him. It was the angel who commanded Hélias to become a knight, to go to Lillefort and fight the awesome Sir Macaire who had asked for a champion. Matabrune and Sir Macaire had arranged to have Queen Béatrix burned at the stake unless a champion appeared to vindicate her. The angel revealed to the hermit and to Prince Hélias the story of his birth.

Prince Hélias, dressed in leaves just as the angel found him, traveled to Lillefort where, after many encounters, countless difficulties, and a long and bloody battle, he vanquished Sir Macaire, proved his mother's innocence, and caused Matabrune to deliver up the five chains and then be burned alive. As soon as the prince put the five chains about his brothers' and sister's necks, they became young ones again. King Oriant and Queen Béatrix fell into each other's arms. They embraced their princely son, turned the kingdom over to him, and spent all their time educating their five children, who were named Rose, Esmerés, Galerant, Alexandre, and Baldwin de Sebourg. Since Prince Hélias did not know of the silver goblets, he could not change his last brother into a prince. Nor did Prince Hélias desire to remain and rule his father's kingdom.

"Now hear," said he, "all my decision. I wish at this time to take leave of you all. Although I have received the crown from my father King Oriant, I shall leave you here; I shall go forth at the command of Jesus to seek adventure in distant lands. Look there, lords, and see the ship moving across the waters. It comes for me, and I must depart. Do you see my brother? He is the lordly swan who pulls my ship. I shall go to him and leave you all to God."

As a parting gift King Oriant gave Hélias, the Swan Knight the magic horn. When it was sounded, no harm or injury could ever befall his son. . . . The song of the swan was marvelous and loud. Four times sang the swan before the knight stepped aboard. Those on shore watched swan, ship, and knight disappear and vanish down the river.

Lords, straight to Nimègue, as I heard the story told, came before the emperor of Germany, Ardennes, Liége, and Namur the very great and dreaded Count of Blanquebourg. This aforesaid lord wished to oust from her lawful and hereditary holding the Duchess Clarisse de Bouillon. Therefore the lady duchess had also repaired to the emperor's court where she intended to appear in her own defense. She had brought her young and very lovely daughter with her.

In order to hear this most important case, the emperor had convoked his assembly. For two days the court had been hearing the pleas. All twelve peers of the realm were also in attendance. Their lawyers, for the plaintiff and the defendant, were at their places. The count's lawyer began his brief: "Be so kind as to hearken to the plea of this noble count whom all must love, and prepare to accord him his due. If you ever had need of aid against enemies of war, he could come to your immediate assistance with 300,000 men—or more. It is he who has had summoned before this court that lady who styles herself of Bouillon a duchess. Her cause is evil, and we must oust her.

"We say that she did feed her husband, brother of this count here present, such herbs as killed him. Now the lands of the deceased, which it is very simple to prove, came from the father of the deceased—may his name be praised—to this duke who died, whom she murdered. Therefore this lady has no right to remain in Bouillon, nor her daughter either, who has no legal claim. For three years the Duke of Bouillon was overseas in the Holy Land, during which period of time he never was able to return home. And at the end of these three years was born this girl. Now one can see clearly that a woman cannot carry a child for a period of three years. By this calculation, we undertake to prove the daughter a bastard.

"These are the reasons we ask the court to ponder solemnly. We rest our case upon them and ask that the lady and her daughter be disinherited and evicted."

The emperor said, "Have the plaintiff swear."

Then a president said loud and clear, "Count, were these words said for you?"

"Yes," replied the count, "I can suggest no amendment to them."

"You must prove your facts," said the president.

The lawyer replied, "I am prepared to show evidence."

The lady's lawyer dared not advance one single word, so greatly did he fear the adverse party. And also they had greased his palm.

This lawsuit heard before the emperor was most impressive. The lady of Bouillon was greatly grieved. Her daughter, a lovely girl, was sad at heart. The emperor, who was a kind-hearted man, said very nicely, "Lady, I see before me a deed of very great dishonor, enough to cause your death if you do not make a suitable defense. You understand that the count is accusing you of murder."

Then the count, who should have left well enough alone, spoke one word out of folly. He had arraigned false witnesses well rehearsed and indoctrinated for that occasion. They could have prettied up his plea. However, he had to say something from his smouldering ire.

"Emperor," said the count, "and barons here present, in order that you may not think I plead erroneously, I say in your presence, as God is my witness, that if there is a knight, or a man, or a vavasor who consents this day to receive my challenge, I will fight him with force and vigor and will prove in mortal combat before the emperor that this lady should die a dishonorable death and that she should never be allowed to hold either a castle or a tower in all Bouillon."

"Now that's another way to settle the case," said the emperor. "Lady, the count shows love for you. Instead of basing his plea upon sound testimony and irrefutable evidence, he lets it hang upon a contest of arms. That is a very great generosity on his part. The best recourse you have, Lady, is to seek a champion. I will give you a month from this day."

Although the duchess looked up and down and around, she could find no man who was not afraid. She summoned her vassals in parliament. She spoke to her people. She could not find for gold or for silver or for anything else a man who would take to the field on her behalf.

Then, as the emperor was about to begin the sentence, those in his palace heard the sound of a horn so loud and clear that all were astounded. The blast echoed through the vast hall before it passed into silence. Many left their desks and seats to crowd to the windows. They looked far down the river. They saw the swan, the ship, and the knight.

"Sire, look at the marvel; by God who does not lie, there is upon the river a real, live swan pulling a ship all and easily by itself. And in this ship there is a knight of goodly countenance." The emperor himself went to the window. He leaned out to look. He saw the swan knight with his very own eyes coming at God's command. They saw the swan draw the ship to its mooring.

"Go, some one, good people," said the emperor, "and bring that knight to me so that I may learn his condition and his lineage."

As the courtiers and attendants left the hall to meet the newly arrived knight, the Duchess of Bouillon suddenly remembered a dream. She said to her daughter, "By God in whom we trust, my heart leaps with joy, but I cannot say why it should. It seems that last night when my body was asleep, I was here pleading against this count who accuses me of high treason, and I was in a fire which burned me cruelly. And just as I was in the fire which they kept lighting all around me, there flew overhead a white swan. As fast as the fire caught, the white swan brought water to quench it. Then I saw that from this water a fish descended which was so abundant that all fed upon it. There were enough victuals for from here to Jerusalem. . . . And now I truly believe that this swan will be my sponsor. I pray God that it may be so." As the lady spoke, the swan knight crossed the hall up to the emperor.

"Welcome," the emperor told him. "Where are you from and who are your ancestors?"

"Ask me no more," said the swan knight. "I am from a country that you will never know. I have come here in search of adventure. I shall serve you, if you so command."

"If you seek adventure, here now will you find it. You see before you a lady whom this count accuses of a deed that is mortal, which allows that the lady be burned flanks and sides, and that her beautiful daughter so filled with graces lose Bouillon and all her inheritance. Thus must it ensue if they are not seconded. If you defend them, the lady—as true as God was born—will become a nun and you shall have the daughter whose beauties are so potent. Here is a splendid adventure, if you like."

The swan knight heard the business and saw the shivering lady. He saw the clear-eyed girl with her innocent, candid face. He went up to the duchess and grasped the front panel of her gown. Then very courteously he said, "I conjure you, lady, upon the passion of Our Lord, and upon His mother whose name was Mary, upon the saints of both sexes and upon the innumerable legions of angels that there are in the skies, that you tell me the truth as you know it. Are you accused rightly or wrongly."

"Yes," said Duchess Clarisse, "by all the oaths you mentioned, and may the devil of lower regions have power to bear my body and my soul to his prison, if ever I plotted or did the high treason of which I have been accused before so many barons."

"Lady," said Hélias, "you shall have your champion."

The swan knight made no delay. He said directly to the emperor: "Have him who wishes to destroy this powerful lady step forward. I shall forbid him and go bond for her."

Count Blanquebourg came from the ranks. "Friend, what are you asking? What moves you to be so forward? Disculpate a murderess who never did a good deed in her born days and who poisoned my brother?"

"Vassal," said Hélias, "I render unto you my gauntlet. I'll have you helpless on your back by sundown for fraudulently inculpating a lady because you coveted her lands. Let us combat with naked swords."

The count took up the gauntlet at once and resolutely. The emperor, preparing to set the contest, asked the swan knight, "For what day do you desire this weighty combat?"

"Sire," said Hélias, "I want it now."

Then to the count the emperor said, "When will you do battle?"

"Tomorrow I will take the field," he answered.

"Let it be tomorrow," decreed the emperor.

"Emperor," said the swan knight loud and clear, "kindly hear me. Have us both promptly and so well imprisoned that neither one nor other can escape."

"I accede," said the emperor. Both knights were locked in rooms and guarded by fifteen men-at-arms. The duchess was returned to her prison. A field near Nimègue was prepared for the contest, and a fire was made high in case the count was victorious.

After a long combat the swan knight, crying "Saint George," killed his adversary and was acquitted of his task by the court.

Ly chevalier au Cisne n'y fait ariestée:
A le pucielle vint, et se l'a acolée.
"Bielle, dist Hélyas, a bien fussiés-vous née,
Bien devés iestre à moy, chier vous ay accatée;"
Et la bielle respont: "Je sui bien assenée,
Dieux me laist désierver ceste bonne journée."

Going directly to the maiden, the swan knight embraced her. "Beauty," Hélias said, "as you were well born, you ought now to be mine, for I have purchased you dear."

The beautiful girl replied, "I am favored by Fortune. May God grant me to deserve this day."

"Lady," said the emperor to Duchess Clarisse, "I do here reinstate you in your lands and county."

And the lady, like a sensible person, replied, "I do here settle them upon him who today reconquered them and do give him my daughter destined to be his. Let her from this day forward be proclaimed duchess, for I shall become a nun to serve Jesus Christ, according to my vow."

And the emperor said, "You are well advised." Then before his army he summoned the swan knight of the high fame. "Knights, hear my thoughts. This is now the Duke of Bouillon who will wed this maiden and then do homage for the lands he has acquired."

"Sire," replied Hélias, "tomorrow will I wed this maiden who is as white as a fairy."

The next night, in truth, the swan knight lay with his duchess and engendered a daughter whose name was Idain. This daughter became the mother of Godefroy, of him who delivered Jerusalem and lived to wear a crown.

One day the gently born Duchess of Bouillon wanted to know, desired very much to know, whence this husband she had married really came. Hélias had long before forbidden her to ask. He had told her to be never so daring as to ask his estate or his place of origin. He then had sworn upon the heads of Saints that as soon as she spoke to him of such questions, he would no longer stay by her side.

The duchess had forgotten this thing. For seven full years she had never raised such questions. However, at the end of seven years, certain devils worked an enchantment upon her. Then she thought long hours about her mysterious husband and greatly desired to know. . . . (And you know how it goes in the heart of a woman; whatever one asks her to do, she will do the opposite.)

One night the duchess was in bed with her fabulous husband. Know for sure that she was not happy because she did not have her own way perfectly. Since she had been so long deep in such thoughts, she had to speak. "Sir," said the lady, "please listen. I beg you to accede to my request, out of your great courtesy. From what country are you and of what lineage. Who were your father and your lovely mother? I would be very glad to know. It is only reasonable for you to grant me such answers."

As the duke heard her words, his blood chilled. "Lady," he said, "you shall never know it. Just as I arranged with you, tomorrow—by God, the Son of Mary—I shall depart from your company. I shall remain in these parts no longer. Tomorrow I shall present myself in the vaulted hall of the emperor at Nimègue and there, in presence of his assembled barons, request a legal separation."

When the lady heard him, she began to sob and cry. She ran from her bed and called her household. As she wept she told them, "I have been the cause of my own undoing. I have lost my lord through my own folly." She had them dress Idain and bring her to the chamber.

"Oh, Sire," cried the daughter, "on the Holy Virgin's name, shall I never have a father, never a day in my life? Alas! What shall I do, sweet and loved Virgin? I shall be an orphan then, and have so little consequence?"

"Daughter," said the duke whose heart was sore, "I shall

make my dispositions concerning you before my departure."

Before his assembled vassals, the duke said, "It is my time to go. You shall shortly see the swan and the swan ship arriving. I beg you in the name of Our Lord who suffered for us that you consent to swear and pledge yourselves by oath to aid and protect my wife and daughter, and to defend them and their lands, and to arrange my daughter's marriage. You shall never see me return to Bouillon again." Even as he spoke, he heard the song of the swan ring out and echo strong and clear. "Good people, it is my time to go."

At once those of Bouillon left their work to rush towards the river. They strained their eyes until they saw the white swan and the ship he was pulling. They then said to each other, "We don't know what to think of our lord who now wishes to cut himself off from us or of his swan which knows where to steer the ship. It must be the work of God who knows what He's about. . . . Nobody surely could ever speak of a more loyal prince than ours. He never allows any tax which burdens his people. He discontinued the unfair tithes and tolls. Day by day he lightened our obligations. We can never find a better lord." All the simple people began to cry as they saw their duke set foot upon his ship. Their grief was sincere.

When the noble Duke Hélias boarded his ship, he commended them all to God. Then, as the swan pulled him out into the river, he averted his face. The swan, his brother, greeted him again joyously. . . . The swan knew that the time approached when Hélias would discover the silver goblets and thus transform him also into a knight.

The Duchess of Bouillon and her daughter Idain journeyed to Nimègue. "Emperor," said the lady, "I have lost my husband who wedded me here. Have pity on me or all will go ill. My daughter will be held lightly unless you take pity on us."

The astounded emperor cried, "What, lady? Is your husband dead? Don't conceal this from me."

"No, sire, not dead. Because of me my lord has gone to revisit the lands whence he came when first he came to us. The swan came drawing the ship."

"Why did he become angry with you?" Then the lady confessed what had happened and how she had sinned.

"Oh, lady," said the emperor, "the devil tempted you, just as Eve tempted Adam to eat the apple, thus damning the world." Even as they spoke, all in the place heard the resounding blast of the swan knight's horn. Within a matter of minutes, the fabulous knight was kneeling before the Emperor Othon. Although the emperor pleaded and reasoned, he could not persuade the swan knight to remain with his family any longer.

"Sire," said Hélias, "there are no attenuating circumstances. It is my time to go far to another kingdom. Not only do I know that God so wishes; I also need to depart. Gentle emperor, I cannot stay."

"Have dinner first," invited the emperor.

"I cannot," said the duke. "I hear the swan singing." He kissed his daughter farewell and left his wife unconscious on the floor.

Hélias built a monastery and a castle in the forest of Arden. He called them Bouillon in honor of his wife and daughter. After this was done and after he had changed the last swan into a knight, Hélias took holy vows and became a monk.

IV

ELIDUC

Marie de France

TWELFTH CENTURY

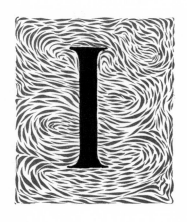

I WILL TELL YOU this story and explain it to you as I have understood it from a very old Breton lay —and to the best of my knowledge.

Once upon a time there was a brave and courteous knight in Brittany, and he was daring and proud. His name was Eliduc as I heard it told. There was not an-other such valiant man in the whole country. He had as his wife and spouse a noble, well-bred woman who had im-portant connections and who came from the high gentry. They lived together for a long time as man and wife. They loved each other faithfully all this time.

It then happened that there was a war in which Eliduc went to serve as a soldier. There he fell in love with a damsel whose name was Guilliadun. The maiden was the daughter to a king and a queen. In the whole realm there was not such a beautiful girl. The wife, whose name was Guildeluec, remained at home in her own country. Because of these two I call my lay *Guildeluec and Guilliadun*. I realize that I mentioned Eliduc's name first, but now their names are reversed, due to their relative importance. Because this adventure came about through the two ladies, I have changed its title. . . . I will tell you the story just as it happened. I want you to know that this is a true story.

Eliduc had as his sovereign lord the King of Small Britain.* This king loved him a great deal and also cherished him. Eliduc served him loyally like a brave vassal. Whenever this king traveled, he put Eliduc in charge of his lands. He kept the knight close to him because of his prowess. However, many things happened to Eliduc despite his good qualities! He could hunt freely through the royal forests, and there was no better forester than he was. No one ever dared cross him or deny him full hunting privileges.

However, out of envy from a third person—and this often happens to a fine man—Eliduc was in some way embroiled with his master. Their relationship grew worse until he was finally openly accused before the king. He was even dismissed from court, for what reason he had no idea. Eliduc could not understand it. Many times he requested the king to give him a legal precedent and not to believe any slander he might have heard. He reminded him of his long and loyal service. But the king would never reply.

When Eliduc saw that the king did not wish to hear any more from him, he decided to go away from court. He left for home, where he summoned all his friends. He showed them the ire which the king bore him. He explained his side

* Brittany in France, not Great Britain.

72

of the story—how he had served him a great deal and to the best of his ability, and that the king should not bear him any ill will. An evil man says by way of excuse that a king's love towards his vassal, when a quarrel arises, cannot be relied upon. That man alone is intelligent and well advised who continues to feel loyalty for his liege lord and love for his good neighbors.

Therefore, rather than invite more trouble, Eliduc decided to cross the Channel and go to the realm of Logre. He planned to remain there for a rather long period of time. He left his wife at home in his own country, entrusting her to the care of his men, and instructing his many friends to protect her together. This solution was no sooner arrived at than put into action. He dressed in his armor and finest robes. His friends were very sorry to see him go.

Eliduc took only ten of his knights with him into Great Britain. He bade farewell to his wife. She wept and sobbed and made all show of grief at this separation. However, he consoled her by protesting that he would be entirely faithful to her. Then he departed with such speed that he soon arrived at the coast, crossed the sea, and landed in Totenois.

This territory was parceled out to many kings among whom there was generally strife and war. In the region called Excester ruled one of these very powerful kings. He was a very old man by this time, however, and he had no male heir to whom he could bequeath his realm. He had only one daughter, a girl of marriageable age. Because this old king did not wish to give her in marriage to another certain king of the region, the latter had waged such a war that he had laid waste most of Excester and shut its king up in one of his castles. Within this fortress there was not a single knight who dared sally forth to engage the enemy king in single combat, or even lead the men of Excester in pitched battle, for that matter.

As soon as he arrived in the land, Eliduc heard of this state of affairs. He saw he would need to travel no further in order to find a new master. Since he had already found a war in which he could use his prowess, he decided to stay right there. He was very anxious to aid the King of Excester with all his power, particularly since this king was so badly beset, so oppressed, and so powerless to defend himself. Eliduc therefore knew he would be rewarded. This would solve his most urgent problem.

Eliduc sent a message to the beleaguered king, telling him also in letters how he had happened to go forth from his native land and how he had come to the king's aid. He also requested to know the king's will in the matter and if he would not care to engage him in his service. He suggested that if such were the case, the king could send him a safe-conduct order through his domains, where Eliduc might also be granted ahead of time the right to levy soldiers.

When the king heard of Eliduc's messengers, he received them lovingly and, indeed, cherished them for the hope they gave him. He called his constable and ordered him to draw up the necessary safe-conduct hastily so that Eliduc could bring his noble barons to him. He also commanded that hostelries be made ready for receiving such vassals and that no expense be spared so that they might be lodged honorably. The documents were drafted. Eliduc was summoned to come at once. The king acknowledged his greeting most cordially. He made the Breton knight feel most welcome.

Eliduc was lodged with a wealthy burgess of the town, a wise and courteous man. His host had prepared for him a splendid bedroom hung with fine curtains. Servants stood ready to do his bidding. Eliduc invited to his table all those knights in the city who were temporarily out of funds. He forbade all of them to receive any payment for their services until the first period of forty days had proved their worth.

During the fourth day of his sojourn in Excester, the cry was raised throughout the city that the enemy had come and that they were fanned out over the surrounding countryside. The rumor had it that they were about to storm the walls and that they had already arrived in force before the main portals. Eliduc could plainly hear all the hue and cry which the city inhabitants were raising. He did not wait long before calling for his armor. He ordered his own knights to prepare for battle along with him. There were in all the town only fourteen knights able to be armed and to sit their horses. There were several wounded knights and, of course, many who had been taken prisoner.

When these able-bodied knights saw Eliduc being dressed in his armor, they returned to their lodgings to prepare also. Without awaiting any summons from him, they rode up to the gate beside him, ready to do battle. "Sire," they said, "we will go forth with you. Whatever you do, we will do also."

"My thanks to you," Eliduc replied. "Would any one of you here know of a narrow passage or ravine where we could catch them at a disadvantage? If we wait for them here, then we will have a chance to joust. But that would not be worth as much as a better plan. We are too few against too many."

The knights replied, "Sire, on our word, near a certain wood there is a narrow defile by which as a rule they pass when they leave the city. As soon as they have made their attack, they usually go home through that pass. Then they are unarmed and mounted on their palfreys. Peradventure they amble home in single file, ripe for attack. We could very quickly do them great damage, wound them, and even defeat them."

"Friends," Eliduc told them, "rest assured that you are protected by my word of honor. Whoever does not often dare go into a tight spot where, for all he knows, he could lose everything—whoever never dares take such a chance—

will hardly rise very high in the world, nor obtain a great position. You are all the king's men and as such owe him your fealty. Come with me wherever I go and do what I will do!

"I assure you in good faith that you will not fall into any great hardship while I am still able to protect you. Even if we are not successful in winning a decisive victory today, we shall do some damage to the enemy."

Because of Eliduc's assurance, the knights all promptly pledged allegiance to him and showed him the way to the woods. They found hiding places close to the road where they could lie in ambush until the enemy returned from Excester. Eliduc had plenty of time in which to instruct his men, to teach them and explain to them the manner in which they should proceed to the attack and how they should surprise the enemy with their combat cries.

As soon as the enemy column was thoroughly engaged in this narrow defile under the trees, Eliduc leaped out shouting his battle cry. He also summoned his comrades whom he urged to attack vigorously. They struck fiercely—to the last man. They did not spare the foe in any way whatsoever. The unsuspecting knights were caught completely off guard. Within a very few minutes they were routed, scattered, and overcome. Eliduc's forces captured the enemy constable and many of the other famous knights. The prisoners were turned over to the squires for safekeeping. Twenty-five prisoners were taken on one side. Thirty more were captured by the other group of Eliduc's men. They also took a marvelous number of rich harnesses and trappings. They made a great haul.

Eliduc and his men trotted back very happily, indeed. They had performed a noteworthy exploit. They saw the King of Excester standing high on one of the towers. He was deathly afraid for his own knights. He was worried, even panic-stricken, because he feared that they had been abandoned or betrayed. He saw a whole troop of knights riding back toward his castle. He saw how loaded their horses were and how tied with huge bundles. There were many more of them returning to the castle than there had been who set forth. Therefore the king was disheartened, doubtful of the success of their enterprise, and very suspicious of their approach. He ordered the gates to be closed and barred. Then he shouted for his men to mount the walls so they would be ready to fire and hurl their missiles upon the approaching party. Fortunately there was no need for any such action.

Eliduc had taken the precaution of sending a squire at top speed ahead of them. This messenger explained the whole engagement to the king, recounted the battle, told how they had vanquished the enemy, and how they had put them to rout. He said that they had even taken the enemy constable, were bringing twenty-nine prisoners with them, and how they had wounded and killed many more.

When the king heard this news, he was overjoyed. He descended the tower stairs and did Eliduc the honor of advancing to meet him. He thanked him for his high deed. Eliduc handed the prisoners over to the king. Among the accompanying knights he divided the spoils, such as the harnesses. For his own use he kept only three of the fine horses they had taken. Then he divided his share of the other booty among his own men and also with the prisoners.

After this deed of which I have spoken to you, Eliduc was dearly beloved and much cherished by the King of Excester. He was retained in his service for the period of a year. Those who had accompanied him across the sea were included in the terms of employment. Eliduc was appointed warder of this king's domains.

Since Eliduc was such an accomplished knight and since his manners were so courteous, the king's daughter heard his name often. She also heard people telling the story of his feats. Through her private chamberlain she required his presence, politely begging him and summoning him to come and entertain her, to speak with her and to make himself known personally to her. She would have been marvelously amazed if he had not rushed into her presence.

Eliduc replied to her message that he would go, that he would very gladly make her acquaintance. He mounted his war horse, took one knight as his escort, and went to converse with the maiden. When he had arrived at the antechamber of her apartments, he sent her chamberlain ahead to announce him. Then Eliduc awaited the chamberlain's return. Then the two together—maiden and knight—with simple manners and very dignified bearings spoke alone most agreeably. Eliduc thanked the damsel Guilliadun—such a pretty girl—that it had so pleased her to summon him to her presence. Meanwhile she had taken him by the hand and drawn him to sit down beside her on a bed. They talked of one thing and another.

Guilliadun looked long and often at Eliduc. She looked at his face, his body, and his bearing. She said to herself, "There is no flaw in him." She particularly esteemed and respected his courage. Love cast his message into her heart and commanded her to adore him. Love made her grow pale and sigh. For his part, Eliduc did not want to have any explanation with her, especially one that would turn her admiration to scorn. He remained sitting in her chamber for a long time. Then he asked her permission and withdrew. He wanted her; he wanted her very much. Nevertheless, he finally left.

He returned, all pensive and mournful, to his *hôtel*. He was fearful even so. This was the daughter of a king. The king was his master. She had called Eliduc so gently to her chamber. She had looked at him and sighed. He was very surprised that he had been so long in the country without ever having seen her before. Even as he thought such thoughts, he remembered his wife whom he had assured of

79

his loyalty and fidelity. He had promised her that he would win over temptation.

The damsel, meanwhile, had already decided to have Eliduc as her sweetheart. She had never before been so impressed by a man. She had already set about making him hers. All that night she neither rested nor slept. As soon as it was daylight, she went to her window and called her chamberlain. She explained her desire and intentions to him. "On my word," she said, "I am lovesick! I have fallen ill with a serious sickness. I love my father's new soldier, the good knight Eliduc! All night long I have not been able to sleep . . . nor even close my eyes. If he wishes to love me with true love and promise his body to me, I will meet all his desires. Great good can come of it as far as he is concerned, for he will then inherit the kingship of this land. He is so fine and so courteous that if he will not love me with true love, then I shall have to die from my deep grief!"

When she had revealed her situation to the chamberlain she had summoned, he gave her such honest advice as could not miscarry. "Lady," he said, "since you are in love with him, send and entrust to him either a belt or a ribbon from your gown or a golden ring. Send something to him. We shall see if he takes it well. For if he receives it willingly and appears joyous because of this honor entrusted to him, then be sure of his love! There is not an emperor under the sky who would not be overjoyed with the gift of your love, wherever you wish to bestow it."

After she had listened carefully to this advice, the royal maiden asked, "How shall I know from this present that he is inclined to love me? I never saw a single knight invited by such a prayer—whether he loved or whether he hated— who did not gladly keep a valuable present sent unsolicited to him. I should hate to have him make a laughing stock of me. Is there no way of reading a man's secret dispositions on his face? Leave me now and go to him!"

"Lady, I am ready to go."

"You will give him this sash and this golden ring from me. And you will greet him a thousand times in my name."

The chamberlain left the lady at once. She stood there hesitating, not sure whether she should let him go or call him back. She finally wavered so long that she had allowed him to go. When there was no longer any possibility of retracting her decision, then she was overcome by panic. "Alas! how suddenly my heart was overcome! How taken by surprise was my heart, unused to a foreigner's manners! I don't even know whether he is of noble lineage. Perhaps he will just disappear all of a sudden. Then I will remain here languishing without him. I fell in love wildly, and wildly made such a pact. I never before yesterday ever saw this man. I had never even spoken to him. And look at me now! Now I am praying him to love me.

"I feel sure he will disapprove of me. If he is a courteous knight, then, of course, he will be grateful to me. Therefore everything now hangs in the balance. And if he has no care for my love, I shall never forgive myself for having acted in such a way. I shall never be able to stop grieving."

As much as she tormented herself, so much the chamberlain hastened to do his commission. He went to Eliduc. He greeted him affectionately as the damsel had instructed him to do. He presented him with the golden ring and with the maiden's sash. The knight took them and thanked the officer. He put the golden ring on his finger. He wound the sash about his waist. He said nothing more to the lady's servant, and the servant asked him nothing. He extended a gift, but the chamberlain did not accept the sum.

The officer returned at once to his mistress where she waited in her chamber. He told her Eliduc's words of salutation and gratitutde. "Say it," she said. "Hide nothing from me. Does he wish to love me truly?"

"That is my opinion of it," the chamberlain replied. "This

knight is not an expansive person. I consider him courteous and moderate, the kind of man who knows how to mask his great courage. I saluted him on your behalf and presented him with your treasures. He wrapped your sash about him, winding it tightly about his hips. Then he slipped your ring on his finger. I said no more to him, nor he to me."

"Yes, but did he not interpret it as signs of a liaison? If that is the case, then I am betrayed."

He replied, "On my word, I don't know. You only hear what I can say. If he did not wish you every good, he would not have taken your possessions."

"You talk just to hear yourself," she said. "I know perfectly well that he doesn't dislike me. I never did him any injury except to love him as hard as I do. And if he hates me for that, then he deserves to die. Never more either by you or by anyone else except through my lips alone shall anything ever be asked of him now. I myself now desire to show him how distressed I am—and all for the love of him. But I don't know if he returns my love."

"Lady," replied the chamberlain, "the king has by solemn oath retained him here in service for the period of a year. He must acquit himself. You will therefore have all the leisure you require for explaining your pleasure to him."

When she heard that Eliduc was remaining, she was most joyous. His long stay at Excester was the best news she could have heard. She had no inkling of how much he was suffering since he first laid eyes on her. From that moment the only joy and delight he could feel came from thinking of her. He was engulfed in bitter thoughts because he had sworn to his wife when he turned away from his native land that he would never love another but her. Now his heart shivered madly for longing to keep its troth faithfully. However, he could not drive from himself the realization that he was deeply in love with the damsel Guilliadun who was so lovely. He only desired to see her and to speak to her and to kiss her and to embrace her. He never could ask for her love except by turning this love into dishonor. He knew he was obliged to keep faith with his wife on the one hand and with the English king on the other hand.

Eliduc was suffering torments. He did not remain in his chamber. He went up the stairs and called his companions. Then he went to the castle to speak to the king. His idea was to see the damsel if he could. This was the reason for his unrest.

The king had just left the table. His daughter entered the room. The king sat down and began to play chess with a baron from overseas. His daughter remained on the opposite side of the chess board. Eliduc crossed the room to where she was. The king looked up and greeted him cordially. Then he asked Eliduc to sit down beside them. He spoke to his daughter. "Mistress," he said, "you should become acquainted with this knight and do him every honor. There is not another one like him in five hundred."

When the maiden heard what her own father bade her to do, she was very happy. She moved away from the chessboard and called Eliduc to her. The two found a seat all to themselves. They were both very much in love. She did not dare begin to explain or confess what she felt for him. Eliduc hesitated to speak except to thank her in person for the presents she had given him. He said no things had ever been so dear to him before in his life.

She told him that she found him handsome and entirely worthy of such gifts. She added that while she only sent him a sash and a ring, it was really her person that she was offering him. She confessed that she loved him with such a love that she wanted to make him her lord and master and that if she could not have him she knew one thing for sure: she would never have any other living man. Then she expressed to him the extent of her feeling.

"Lady," he replied, "I am very much indebted to you for

83

your love. It brings me great joy. When I realize how high a worth you assign to me, it is only natural for me to be at the height of happiness. My love for you will never cease. I have sworn to remain for one year in the service of the king, and he has my solemn oath upon it. I shall therefore not depart from this land until the war is won and ended. Afterwards I shall return to my own country, for I should not care to remain here longer, if I may then have your leave to depart."

The maiden replied, "Dear friend, I thank you greatly. You are so fine and so chivalrous. You have certainly already decided what you wish to do with me. I love you and trust you in every respect."

Thus they reassured each other. They spoke no more at that meeting. Eliduc returned to his lodging. He was henceforth very happy. He had acted perfectly well thus far. He was very glad to be able to speak to his love often. The love between them was ardent. Eliduc, meanwhile, pressed the advantage he had already won in the war so cleverly that within a short time he had defeated the king's enemies and had gained back all the disputed land. He was so esteemed for his prowess, for his intelligence, and for his generosity that everyone said how fortunate it was for them that he had come.

At about this time Eliduc's own king in Brittany began to search for him and actually sent him three letters from across the sea. He told Eliduc how he was heavily beset by rebellious lords, how he had been attacked, damaged, beaten worse and worse. He said he was losing all his fine castles and, what was even harder to bear, was seeing his fine domains stolen from him or laid waste. He added that he had often had occasion to regret Eliduc's departure, that he had certainly been ill-advised, that he had listened to malicious counselors who had caused him to regard such a good knight with disfavor. He also told Eliduc that he had expelled from his lands and sent into permanent exile all the traitors who had formerly accused him, stained his reputation, and meddled in his affairs. Because of his great and present difficulties he required Eliduc and summoned him and begged him even—by the oath he once swore when he first made vows of fealty—to come to his aid because he was really in very great trouble.

Eliduc heard this news. He was especially sad to learn it because of the damsel. He loved her most desperately, and she loved him as much as anyone could ever love. However, there never had been any foolishness between them, no stepping over the bounds of propriety, and no villainy. To exchange tokens and to speak to each other, to give each other their most beautiful possessions was all the love-making they had ever done—and this for love—in each other's company. Their mutual understanding was all their trust and hope. She thought she possessed him absolutely and had the power to keep him near her. She was unaware of the fact that he had a wife.

"Alas!" he said. "My wandering days are over! I have stayed too long in this country! It was an ill day when I first saw it! And here I have loved a maiden, Guilliadun, daughter of the king. And I have loved her greatly, and she me. When it shall be necessary for me to leave, one of us will have to die, or as it may even be, both of us. Yet, nevertheless, I am forced to go. My lord has ordered me in a brief and commanded me according to my feudal oath, and there is also the oath which, on the other hand, I made to my wife. Now I shall do well to be on my guard! I can stay here no longer. I shall have to go. Christianity would never allow me to wed my sweetheart. Whatever I do, it will end badly. Our separation comes by the will of God. But however He may hold me up as blameworthy, I will always know He has every right to do so. I shall obey His will and guide my actions according to His counsel.

"This king of Excester now rules a land at peace. Because of my own lord's perils I shall ask for permission to depart before the term of my service expires. I will also go speak to the damsel and show her the state of my affairs. She then will say what her will is, which I shall fulfill to the best of my ability."

Eliduc did not delay. He went directly to the king to ask for his discharge. He recounted to him the whole story of what had happened to his king in Brittany, showed him the brief sent in such distress from his lord. The king of Excester understood the gravity of such a summons. He realized that Eliduc could not remain with him any longer. He was sad and aggrieved. From his own wealth he liberally offered a third part even of his entire inheritance. He offered him all his treasury, asking him to remain if he could, thus earning also for himself an everlasting praise for liberality.

"In God's name," replied Eliduc, "at this time and since my Sire in such distress has summoned me from so far away, I shall have to go about his business. I shall not remain here in any fashion whatsoever. If you should have other difficulties so serious as to require my services again, I will return willingly and bring with me a large force of knights-at-arms."

The king thanked him for this and very graciously granted him leave to depart. He put at his disposal all the wealth of his castle—gold and silver, dogs and horses, and beautiful and goodly silken fabrics. In moderation Eliduc helped himself to these presents and then said directly that he would very much like to go speak to the king's daughter, if that were pleasing to His Majesty.

"That is a fine request, and it is granted," replied the king.

A damsel was dispatched ahead of Eliduc to notify the king's daughter that the knight requested an audience. She

rapped on the chamber door and said the Eliduc was there.
When Guilliadun saw him she called him in immediately.
Six thousand times she greeted him eagerly. Very briefly he
explained his situation to her. Before he had even finished
explaining the affair to her, before he had even asked her
permission to depart, she grew deathly pale and fainted
away before him.

When Eliduc saw her lying unconscious, he went out of
his mind with grief. He began to kiss her mouth often and
to weep very pitifully over her. He lifted her into his arms
and held her close until she had opened her eyes and regained possession of herself.

"God's name," he said, "my sweetheart, please allow me
to speak to you. You are my life and my death. In you lies
all my solace utterly. Because of this I take my consolation
from you since we are affianced one to the other. I go into
my own country out of necessity. For this reason alone I
asked leave of your father, but I will do whatever your
pleasure is, no matter what the consequences may be to me."

> *Par deu, fet il, ma dulce amie*
> *Suffrez un poi que jo vus die*
> *Vus estes ma vie et ma morz*
> *En vus est trestuz mi conforz*
> *Pur ceo preng jeo cunseil de vus*
> *Que la fiance a entre nus.*
> *Pur busuin vois en mun païs*
> *A vostre pere ai cungié pris*
> *Mes jeo ferai vostre plaisir*
> *Que que me deïë avenir.*

"Oh, take me with you," she sobbed, "since you do not
wish to remain here any longer. Or if it is no, then I will
kill myself. I shall otherwise never be joyous again."

Eliduc answered her gently, for he loved her really with
a true love. "Beauty, I am truly bound to your father by a

knight's oath. If I were to take you with me, I would be breaking my vows. We must wait until the term of this oath is ended. I swear to you now and take a solemn oath that if you will consent to grant me a leave of absence and set a certain term upon it and name a day, and if you wish me to return, there is nothing in the world that can hinder me from doing so, provided that I am alive and well. My whole life is between your hands.*

The lady therefore had his great love. She set a term for his leave and named a day for him to come and take her away with him. There was great sorrow as they tore themselves apart. They exchanged golden rings and very gently kissed each other good-bye.

Eliduc went across the sea. He had a very good wind and passed over quickly. When he presented himself at court, his king was joyous and very glad to see him. So were his friends, and his relatives, and his companions, and especially his good wife who was so beautiful, so noble, and so well-bred.

Day after day, however, Eliduc was pensive because of the new love that had taken his heart unawares. Nothing he saw, wherever he happened to go, could even bring a smile to his face, to say nothing of making him really happy. He could never be really glad until the day he saw his sweetheart again. However, he contained himself subtly.

His wife was heartsick. She no longer knew what she ought to do. She also kept her complaints to herself. She often wondered if her husband could have heard from any person that she had been unfaithful or guilty of other misconduct while he was out of the country. She often asked him if this was the case. She said she was willing to justify her conduct before any persons he might name, or before her own household, whenever such action would please him.

* Ma vie est tute entre voz meins. (vs. 696)

"Lady," he told her, "nobody considers you either unfaithful or otherwise guilty of misconduct or mismanagement. But I swore in the country where I have been and I pledged that king that I would return, for there is a great demand for my services in that land. If my lord and king were at peace here, I wouldn't stay here even for eight days. I must go through many hardships over there before I can return. Therefore I can take no delight here no matter where I go or what I see until I have returned there as I swore to do. I will not break this solemn oath." Eliduc left his wife alone as much as he could.

Eliduc also remained near his king, rather than at home. He aided him greatly and proved his worth. The king on his side followed his vassal's advice and assigned Eliduc all his lands to guard. However, before the day which the maiden had named approached, Eliduc undertook to establish peace. Then he set about choosing those of his men whom he wanted to have accompany him. He enlisted two of his nephews of whom he was particularly fond and also his own chamberlain. This latter had given him good advice on many occasions and had also already carried a message from him into England. Then he enrolled his own squires. He asked all these men to promise, to pledge, and to swear that they would keep the business he had at hand a perfect secret. He cared to have none but them with him.

Without further delay he embarked for overseas. His preparations had been hastily made. He arrived without hindrance in the land where he was so desired. Once there, Eliduc took every precaution. He avoided the harbors where he usually dropped anchor. He took care not to be recognized and not even to be seen. He intended no one to find him. He made his chamberlain ready and then dispatched him to the lady. He instructed the officer to say that he had come as he had promised to do, and that he had kept his covenant with her. He said that as soon as it was dark enough, he would prepare to leave the city, that his chamberlain would be with him, and that their meeting would be then.

This chamberlain had purchased other garments and dressed in them. He walked into the city so as not to attract attention. He went directly to the lady's quarters. He sought and bought so carefully that he made his way inside her private apartments. He bowed low in salutation and told the maiden that her lover had come. When the girl heard this news, her eyes filled with tears. She was astonished. She sat crying with joy, and she kissed the kind messenger often. He told her that when it was dark he would manage to take her out of the city with him.

All that day the two of them remained quietly in her quarters making their plans.

After the stars had come out that night, they stole out of the city—the royal maiden and the chamberlain—only the two of them. She took no attendants with her. She was terribly afraid of being recognized. She had thrown over herself an ample cloak of dark silk, heavily embroidered with gold. Under that she wore a surcoat.

About the distance of an arrow shot from the city gate there was a very pretty wood enclosed in a park. Her lover was waiting for her close to the palisade. He had come back only for her. The chamberlain led her over the dark grass to the park. Her lover climbed down from the wall. He kissed her. That was a happy reunion! Then Eliduc lifted her on a horse, mounted behind her, gathered the reins, and set off at top speed.

He headed straight for the harbor of Totenois where they went aboard without losing a second. There was not a man who saw them, no one but Eliduc, Guilliadun, and the chosen comrades. The wind blew fresh. The weather held fair. The sea was level and calm until they approached the Breton coast. There they ran into a violent storm.

The wind blew so hard from landward that they were driven away from the harbor mouth and back out to sea. Their yards split and broke. All the canvas was ripped off her.

Those on board knelt down to pray. Devoutly they called on Saint Nicholas and Saint Clement and the Holy Virgin Mary who prays to her son for them all, that they might be kept from perishing and that they might safely make the harbor. Their ship was blown an hour or so in one direction until an opposite wind sped them back again and across the harbor entrance. Thus they flew along the coastline. Many times they were close to shipwreck.

Then one of the crew cried out in a loud voice, "What are we doing here anyway? Sire, you have aboard with you the woman for whom we must all perish. We shall never make it to dry land! You have a faithful wife of your own at home, and yet despite this you are bringing another one over with you, contrary to God and to the law, contrary to all right and to all honor. . . . Let us throw her overboard into the sea. If we do that, then we shall make it to shore."

Eliduc heard what the man said. He was suffused with rage. "Whoreson," he cried. "Evil man. Treacherous felon. Don't say another word. If I were free to leave my sweetheart alone here, I would pay you back dearly!" But he was holding her in his arms at the time and comforting her as best he could; first because she was so seasick and frightened, all the more lovingly since she also had heard the sailor say that Eliduc had married a woman other than her—other than his dear love—in his own country over the sea.

Guilliadun fell suddenly forward on her face. As pale as death, without a tinge of pink in her cheeks, she lay unconscious in his arms. Despite Eliduc's efforts to arouse her, the girl hardly breathed. She did not regain consciousness. She did not even sigh. The companions of Eliduc came close to examine her. They all thought she was dead for sure. They were overcome with sorrow at the sight of her pitiful, white face.

Eliduc laid her down gently. Then he stood up. He made his way across the deck to the sailor who had spoken. With an oar, Eliduc struck him such a blow that the fellow sprawled his full length. Then leaning down, Eliduc grabbed one of his legs, lifted him, and cast him overboard into the raging sea. He watched the waves grab the body and bear it out of sight as soon as he released it. Then Eliduc went astern and took the tiller. He held it so firmly and set such a good course that before long the ship passed between the headlands and entered the harbor. As soon as they had come up to the quay, he tied her up and dropped anchor.

Guilliadun still lay exactly as he had left her. She had made no stir. She was exactly as if dead. Eliduc leaned over her. He was broken with grief. The wish of his life lay dead with her. He asked his friends if they could give some advice as to where he could carry the damsel. For he said that he would never leave her side until he saw that she was properly entombed and laid to rest with great honor, with a splendid service, and buried in a blessed cemetery plot. She had been in life the daughter of a king. Such ceremonies were her due. . . . The companions of Eliduc were at a loss for words and ideas. They could think of no good counsels.

Eliduc searched his mind for a suitable place where he could bear her. His own estates were close to the seashore where he had steered the ship. He was so near home that he could be there in time for dinner. Around his own manor house stretched a thick forest about thirty leagues in length. . . . In this forest lived a holy hermit who had his own small chapel. He had lived there for forty years. Eliduc had often stopped to converse with him.

"I'll take her to him," Eliduc said. "He will bury her in his chapel. I will then give him so much land that he will be able to found an abbey in her honor and build there also a convent for monks and a convent for nuns, and there will be canons who will recite prayers for her every day. May God grant her mercy from His good grace!"

Then Eliduc called for his horses to be brought down to the shore. He had his companions mount. He also required each one of them to swear that he would never reveal a thing of what had happened.

Eliduc mounted and then took his sweetheart's body in his arms before him on his palfrey. He rode ahead of the others with her into the woods, keeping to the straight path until he came to the hermit's chapel. There he dismounted and knocked on the door. There was no answer. He knocked and beat upon the door. There was still no answer. No one came to open the door. Then Eliduc sent one of his men to climb inside and unbolt the door. They found upon entering that the holy hermit, that perfect man, had gone to his rest about eight days previously. They even found his grave, covered with fresh earth. Eliduc was very sad. He was dismayed at the loss of the holy man. . . . The companions wanted to dig a grave for the sweetheart, but Eliduc told them to stand back, away from her.

"No," Eliduc told them, "that is not my desire. Before I decide what to do, I shall ask advice of the elders and fine people of the country as to how I can beautify this spot with a splendid abbey or a cathedral. Then I will place her under the high altar and recommend her soul to God."

Eliduc told his friends to fetch robes and blankets and linens. He made a soft bed for the damsel there in the lonely chapel and laid her to rest on it. The others helped him. They took leave of her. They left her for dead. . . . When Eliduc came to the moment of leaving her, he thought he would die from grief. He kissed her eyelids and her face.

"Beauty," he said, "if it so please God, may I never bear arms again. May I not live long nor last long in this century. . . . Beauty, it was an ill day for you when you first saw me. Sweetheart, you followed me to your misfortune! . . . Beauty, once you were a queen. There was never a love so loyal and so fine as the love you loved me with loyally. Oh, how sad and mournful is my heart for you. . . . The day that I see you buried, I shall take the vows of a monk. I will then come every day to chant over your tomb the refrain of my sorrow."

Eliduc finally departed from the maiden's side and closed the door to the chapel.

He sent word to his home and announced to his wife that he was coming. He was weary and careworn. When his wife heard that he was home, she was overjoyed. She set about making great preparations to welcome him home. She received her lord most courteously and ceremoniously. There was little joy in it for her, however. He showed no sign of pleasure on his face. He could not say one good word. No one dared ask him the reason. Two whole days he stayed in the house, somber and gloomy. Each morning he heard mass as was his custom. Then he left the house and went off down the road.

Every day he went to the chapel where the damsel lay on her bed. Every day he found her cold and still. She did not regain consciousness. She did not breathe. There was one thing that amazed him greatly: the fact that he saw her pink and white. She was only a little bit pale. She had hardly lost her pretty colors at all. He stayed there beside her and wept. He prayed fervently for her soul. When he had said his prayer, then he returned home again.

One day, as he came out of the minster from mass, his wife set one of her valets to watch him. She instructed the servant to follow him from afar and to see, if he could, where his master went and by what route. She promised her valet arms and horses if he were successful. He obeyed her instructions. First he hid at the entrance to the wood.

Then he followed the master so well that he was unobserved. He looked closely and saw how he entered the chapel. He also heard him mourning and sobbing inside. The valet waited until Eliduc came out of the chapel. Then he went home to his mistress. He told her of the master's grief, and how he cried, and how he sobbed there alone in the lonely hermitage.

The lady took her courage in hand. "Let us go at once! Let us hunt all around the hermitage. Milord must be in trouble, as I see it. He now says he is going up to court to speak to the king. The hermit died quite some time ago. I know perfectly well that milord was fond of him, but he would never do such things for the hermit. He would never carry on in such grief for him."

This time she let her husband go. That very day, after noon, Eliduc went up to speak to the king. The lady took her valet with her. He led her to the hermitage.

When the lady entered the chapel, she saw the damsel lying on her bed. The girl resembled a new-blown rose. The lady bent down and lifted off her coverlet. She saw the beautiful, slim body. She saw her long, white arms. She saw her lovely hands, her thin fingers, long and rounded. Then she knew the truth. Then she knew why her lord was so deep in mourning. She called the valet to her and showed him the marvel.

"Do you," she said, "see this woman who in beauty resembles a gem? This is the sweetheart of milord, for whom he feels such pain. On my word, I do not wonder at it when such a beautiful woman has perished. As much out of pity as from love for her, I too will never feel joy again."

The lady began to weep and lament for the maiden. She sat down by the bed and cried.

Just then a little mouse, which had come out from the altar, ran across the floor. As it passed, the valet struck it with his staff and threw it into the middle of the room.

When its mate ran out also and saw the place where she lay, he went over to the crushed body and touched its head and prodded its body. When he saw that he could not rouse his mate, he acted as if he felt sorrow and was weeping. Then the male mouse darted outside the chapel into the long grass beside the woods. He picked a flower in his teeth—a blossom of a bright crimson color. Quickly he came back inside the hermitage. He placed the flower in such a way between the teeth of his mate, which the valet had slain, that instantly the little mouse re-lived.

The lady watched this happen. She cried to the valet, "Stop her! Toss your stick, good man. Don't let her get away!" And he tossed the stick so as to jar the flower from the mouse's teeth. The flower fell to the floor. The lady stood up and took it in her fingers. She quickly went back to the bed. In the maiden's mouth she put the flower, between those lovely lips. For a few monutes nothing happened. Then the damsel began to stir. She sighed. Then she murmured. She opened her eyes.

"God," she said, "I have slept so long!"

When the lady heard her speak, she began to thank God. Then she asked the maiden who she was.

"Lady," the maiden replied, "I was born in Logres, the daughter of that country's king. A knight loved me very much. His name was Eliduc. He was a good soldier. He took me away together with him. He had committed a sin by which he tricked me. He had already married another woman, and he did not tell me so nor even let me know it by any of his actions towards me. When I heard tell of his wife, I had to faint away from sorrow. Now discovered in this ugly way, he has abandoned me here in a strange land. He has betrayed me, and I don't know what to do. . . . That damsel is insane who puts her trust in a man!"

"Beauty," the lady answered her, "there is not a living thing in this world which can now bring him joy. And I can tell you that for the truth. He believes that you are dead, and his grief is marvelous to behold. Every day he has come here to gaze upon you. He knows that he found you unconscious day after day. . . . In truth, I am his wife, and my heart aches much for him. Because of the sorrow that made him desolate, I wanted to find out where he went. I came here after him and so found you. . . . I am very happy that you are alive. I will take you away from here with me, and I will return you to your love. I wish to settle the whole matter once and for all, and I will take the veil over my head."

The lady so comforted the damsel that she was finally able to persuade her to come along home with her. The lady, meanwhile, instructing her valet as to how he should say it, dispatched him to find the master.

The valet found Eliduc, greeted him, and recounted the whole adventure. Eliduc called for his horse, did not wait for his escort to saddle up, and was home by nightfall. When he saw for himself that his sweetheart was alive, he thanked his wife most sweetly. He was overjoyed. He had never before in his life been so happy. He kissed the damsel and kissed her, and she him gently. They were together and therefore blissful.

After the lady saw how they behaved towards each other, she had an explanation with her husband. She sued him for permission, which he granted, that she might leave him. She wanted to become a nun and serve God, she said. She asked also that her lord settle certain of his lands upon her so that she could have an abbey constructed. She said for him to take the one he loved so much, for it was not fitting that he maintain two wives—nor, indeed, did the law permit such a thing. Eliduc freely granted all her requests and gave her leave to depart. He agreed to do all her wishes, including the transfer of property.

He had a minster erected for her near the chapel and

hermitage in the forest, and he constructed all the buildings
for her abbey as agreed. He settled upon her vast tracts of
land and great wealth, largely sufficient for all her necessi-
ties. When all was finished and ready, the lady took the veil
and holy vows along with thirty other sisters. She established the rules of her order, thus regulating her own
life.

Eliduc then wedded his sweetheart with great honor, in
a beautiful ceremony. And great were the festivities he had
arranged for his wedding day! They lived together many
days. The love between them was ever a perfect, flawless
love. They gave away large sums in alms and were always
benefactors of the poor. . . . Finally the time came when
both were truly awakened to the faith.

Eliduc had constructed a magnificent church where he
lavished all his gold and all his silver. This church ad-
joined his castle. He put into its construction all his experience and his foresight. He added all his lands to its hold-
ings. Then he founded a monastery near by where he re-
cruited men of the finest he could find to take vows and
obey its holy order. When all was established, Eliduc, in his
turn, without unnecessary delay, joined them, gave himself,
rendered himself also up to Almighty God. . . . He arranged for his beloved sweetheart to join his first wife in
her abbey.

The lady received Guilliadun like a sister. She showed her
every sign of affection, love, and deference. She encour-
aged her to serve God loyally, and she herself taught her
new sister the rules of their order. The two ladies prayed
God to show His mercy to Eliduc, who also was praying for
them. He often sent messages to them to hear how they
were. Each lady supported and comforted the other.

The three separately endured much pain in order to show
that their love of God was in good faith. Each one had a
very good end, for which I thank God, the truly divine.

Ancient Bretons, schooled in courteous love, made this lay of the adventure which befell the three of them. They made it so they would be remembered. Therefore, let us not forget their story.

V

YONEC

Marie de France

TWELFTH CENTURY

INCE I started writing lays, this work shall never be left aside for any other. I shall continue to tell you in rhyme all the adventures I know. I have these days in my thoughts and in all my desires the story of Yonec. First I will tell you whose son he was—of what father and mother—and how he came to be born upon this earth. The man who engendered Yonec was named Muldumarec.

Long ago in Brittany there lived a very rich man who was old and feeble. He was the owner of a place called Caervent and was, therefore, held far and near as its lord. The city was on a river, but it was not a pleasant place, this old man's inheritance. It was old like him.

Now since this old lord had no heir to whom he could leave his riches, he took a wife just so he would beget a child. The maiden was chosen from a noble family. So this well-bred, courteous, and extremely beautiful girl was given to the old, rich man. He loved her for her great loveliness. Why should I dwell upon this situation? There wasn't another girl so remarkably beautiful from there into Ireland. It was a great sin to have given her to him.

Because the maiden was so beautiful and so gentle, the old man put all his intelligence to work as to how he could keep her. He had her shut up in a room with a tiled floor, and this room inside a tower. Then he had his sister come to guard the girl. This sister's husband was long dead. She also was old and a widow. This was the girl's only companion. There were, of course, other women attendants. At least, I think so. But they were in a separate chamber apart, and the girl could never even speak to them unless the old women granted her permission to do so.

For seven long years and more—and they never had any children—the poor girl never once set foot outside the chamber, not even for her relatives, not even to visit a friend. When the lord went to bed with her, there was neither chamberlain nor valet who so much as dared enter the chamber—to say nothing of carrying a lighted candle before him.

The lady lived out her years in a state of great lethargy. Because of her tears and her sighs and her cries, she lost her looks just as anyone does who can't care any longer. As far as she was concerned, she wished that death would hurry and come and take her.

One time, towards the early days of April when the little birds were singing for spring, the lord got up one morning. He decided to go out into the forest. He made the old woman get up also to unlock the door for him and to bolt it after he had gone. She did as he bade her. Then she

102

went out into another room with her psalter to recite her verses.

The lady was awake. She lay there crying in the spring sunlight. Even though the old woman had left the chamber, she could still keep an eye on her prisoner. The lady complained and sighed. "Alas," she said, "that I was ever born—to have such a wretched life. My destiny is a hard one! I am in prison here in this tower, and I shall never get out as long as I live. What is the matter with this jealous old man? What does he fear? Why does he keep me under such strict guard? He is crazy and confused. Every day he fears he will be betrayed. I can't even go to the minster and hear services in honor of God. If I could talk to people and go out to a party with him, I would show him how nicely I would behave, even if I didn't have a good time.

"May my parents be cursed and everybody else, too, who gave me to this jealous old man. And damned be those who married me to his body also! He ties me with a tight cord always pulled tighter. He will never be ready to die. The day they baptized him they must have dipped him in the river of hell. That's why his nerves and his veins are so rigid. They are all full of red blood.

"Now I have often heard tell that in the old days people in this country had adventures which were so exciting that they beguiled them from their gloomy thoughts. Knights found damsels who were gentle and lovely and to their taste. Ladies found lovers who were handsome, courteous, fearless, and valiant. The ladies never lost their reputations because they alone knew they had lovers. Nobody else saw anything.

"If that can happen to me as it used to happen, or if it ever did really happen that way to anyone, dear God, who has power over all, let it be done according to my wishes!"

Just as she finished her complaint, the shadow of a huge

104

bird fell across her narrow window. She could not imagine what it was. The bird flew closer and then right into the room. It had jesses on its feet. It seemed to be a falcon. It seemed to have molted five or six times. The bird alighted right before the lady. After it had sat there for a while and she had observed it, the bird was transformed into a handsome and gentle knight.

The lady did not believe it. Without moving or even having time to speak, she quaked with fear. Suddenly she threw her veil over her head. The knight, however, was very soft-spoken. He began at once to explain himself to her. "Lady," he said, "do not be afraid. A falcon is a gently-bred bird, even if its secrets are presently hidden from you. Look up and see how safe you are. Please have me as your lover!"

"That is why I came here. I have been in love with you for a very long time. In my heart I have desired you also. I have never loved another woman before you, and I shall never love any other but you. But I was never able to come to you before and never before able to go out of my own country . . . until today when you summoned me to fly to your side. Now you see that I am your love."

The lady began to be reassured. She uncovered her face and began to speak. She answered the knight, saying that she would take him as her sweetheart if he believed in God and if he had really come from his country so that their love could be. . . . Meanwhile, she admired him. Never in any day of her life had she seen such a handsome knight. She also knew that she never again would see another half so handsome.

"Lady," he told her, "you speak well. I should not wish for anything in the world to cast any doubts or arouse any suspicions. I certainly do believe in the Creator who lifted us out of the sorrow where Adam cast us, Our Father, when he bit into that sour apple. He always will be and always was the life and the light for sinners. If you do not believe my word in this matter, ask your chaplain. Say that you suddenly do not feel well and that you want to hear divine services which God established here on earth to guarantee sinners from perdition. I will take on your form and will receive in your stead the holy sacrament. Then I will have made my confession before you, and you will have no more doubts about me."

Then she lay down on the bed beside him, but he did not wish to touch her, nor to embrace her, nor to kiss her. They stayed there until the old woman returned into the chamber. She looked in the bed and saw that the lady was awake. She told her it was time to get up. She said she would bring her clothing. The lady replied that she was ill. She asked the old woman to hunt for the chaplain and have him come to her at once since she was afraid that she would die.

The old woman replied, "Oh, lie there and suffer! Milord has gone out in the forest. During his absence no one shall enter this chamber except me."

When she understood this refusal, the lady panicked. She then pretended that she had fainted away. The old lady was persuaded. She, too, became frightened. She unbolted the door of the chamber and called for the old priest. He came running as fast as he could, bringing the *corpus domini* with him.

It was the knight in the lady's form who received the sacrament; he who drank the wine also. The chaplain departed. The old lady, also. The door was bolted.

The lady lay beside her lover. Never did anyone see such a handsome couple. After they had laughed and played long enough and spoken enough about their secret talk, the knight asked leave to depart. He said it was time for him to return to his own country. The lady asked him to come back often to see her again.

"Lady," he said, "whenever you please. I shall not fail

the hour. But take such precautions as will ensure our continuance without any difficulties. That old woman would betray us. She will watch over this room night and day. She will suspect our love. On the slightest pretext she will tell everything to her lord. If it falls out as I say and if we are betrayed and our love revealed, there will be no way in the world for me to escape. In such an event I shall be obliged to die."

After this warning, the knight went away leaving his sweetheart in great joy. The next morning she arose full of life and health. She could hardly wait for the week to pass. She began to like her own body. She saw that she had recovered her beauty. Those days she no longer minded living alone in the tower. She had no more thoughts of going outside for visits or diversions. She only wanted to see her lover often and to have all her joy from him.

As soon as her lord left her and each time that he left her, then night or day, early or late, she had all her desires fulfilled. (May God give them long days—and many of them!) . . . Because of the blissful state in which she now lived when she could see her lover constantly, all her appearance was transformed.

Her lord took note of this metamorphosis. His second sense warned him that all was no longer as it used to be. He first distrusted the old woman, his sister. One day he brought the matter to a head by challenging her. He told her bluntly that he was most surprised to see the lady so elegantly dressed every day. This was an unaccustomed marvel. He asked the old woman why this was, according to her. She answered that she couldn't imagine, since the lady was kept in solitary confinement where no one could speak to her and where she had neither sweetheart nor admirer. The old woman granted that the lady of her own free will remained alone more uncomplainingly than she had used to do. She had, in fact, noticed that.

107

After a pause, the lord continued to think aloud. "On my faith," he said, "I notice it, too. Now you must do something for me. Tomorrow morning after I have arisen from bed and after I have left the room, pretend that you are going out also. Only pretend to go out and bar the door after you. Pretend that as usual you are letting her lie a while in bed. Instead of leaving the room, go hide in some secret nook. Stay there quietly. Then look. Keep a sharp watch to see what happens. Try to discover what it is and what the reason can be that she is suddenly so very joyous." With this plan settled between them, the two went about their separate ways.

Alas! How unfortunate were the two lovers, those whom the old lady intended to spy upon in order to betray them and trick them!

Three days later, as I heard it told, the lord pretended he had to make a journey. He notified his wife to that effect. He told her a long story about how the king had sent for him by writ. He said he would return home as quickly as he could. Then he left the room, as usual bolting the door after him.

The old woman then got up and tiptoed behind a drapery where she could hear and see without being seen that which she was so covetous to know.

The lady lay in her bed. She did not sleep because she desired her lover so much. . . . And so he came, without any delay and without missing his summons, and the term and the hour. Their joy together was very great, both in word and in appearance, until it was time to get out of bed. At that time he had to leave his love. The old woman saw everything, so closely did she watch. She saw how he came and how he went. Her heart was in her throat when she saw him first a man and then a falcon.

As soon as the lord returned to the castle, which was soon, for he had not meanwhile gone very far away, she told him and explained to him the whole truth about the knight. The lord had much food for thought. He set about having traps built so he could kill the knight. He had his blacksmiths forge four steel jaws which tapered into very sharp, curved hooks in the front. There were not, they decided, such sharp razor edges under the sky. When these traps were completed and tested to see that they sprang shut at the touch, he had them set on the window ledge. They were put side by side and very close together. Then they were bolted to the stone. They completely covered the ledge across which the knight stepped when he came to visit the lady.

God! How terrible that he didn't know the treachery that the murderous lord had forged in his intention!

Early next morning the lord rose from bed, as was his custom, at daybreak. He said he intended to go hunting. The old woman escorted him to the door and then returned to sleep a little more. It was not light enough yet to see clearly. Therefore she knew it was too early to begin the day.

The lady lay waiting for her lover whom she adored. She thought to herself that he would be coming soon. How nice it would be for them to have so much time together. It would be leisurely.

She did not have to wait at all after she asked him to come. After she asked him, he did not wait hardly at all. Through the half light he came flying to the window, but the claws stuck out towards him. One pierced him through the body. His crimson blood poured forth from the wound. Even though he knew he was pierced to death, he pulled himself from the iron tongs and entered the chamber. Before the lady he fell on the bed . . . so heavily that the sheets were all covered with blood. She saw the blood and the wound. In great anguish she moaned and cried aloud.

He said to her, "My sweet love, for loving you have I lost my life! I told you that it would happen this way, that your appearance would kill us."

When she heard him say those words, she fell back in a faint. For a few seconds she lay as if dead. He comforted her gently, telling her that it did no good to grieve. Then he said that she was pregnant by him and that she would have a strong, valiant son to console her. He told her to name the child Yonec. This son would avenge both her and him by killing their treacherous enemy. . . . He said he could not stay any longer. His wound had almost drained him of blood. He left in great pain.

Shrieking loudly, the lady unhesitatingly followed him. She jumped out the window after him. It was a marvel she did not kill herself, for it was twenty feet off the ground. From that height she took a leap and jumped. She was naked under her nightgown. She set herself to follow the traces of blood that had spilled from the knight's wound. She could see them on the path where she was. She followed the drops of blood until she came to a hill.

In this hill there was an entrance. All about was red and dripping with blood. She peered ahead of her. She could see nothing, but she believed her lover had entered there. Mustering her courage, she entered. It was pitch black inside. There was not even a glimmer of light. She felt her way forward so steadily, however, that she finally came out into a beautiful green meadow.

The grass at her feet was splotched with drops of blood. She was dismayed at the sight of it again. Without stopping, however, she followed the traces through the middle of the field. Then, fairly close ahead of her, she saw a city. It was all around enclosed by a wall. Not a house, not a hall, not a tower in it but seemed all made of shining silver. . . . The Prince's residence was most ornate of all. Between her and the burg were pastures and forests and game parks.

Behind them and the keeps was an encircling moat filled with deep water. . . . Ships came all the way there from the sea. She saw more than three hundred and three riding at anchor.

The gate on her side of the city was unbarred. Still following the path of fresh blood, the lady entered the city. She walked through its streets and up to the castle. There was no call and no greeting. No one challenged her. She found neither man nor woman all the way. On the marble floor of the great hall the blood was thicker.

The lady walked until she came to a beautiful chamber. Inside she found a knight asleep. She did not recognize him, so she went forward until she came to a larger chamber. There she found a bed and nothing more. There was a knight asleep on it. She passed through this room also. She walked until she came to a third chamber where she found the bed of her lover. It was the richest room of all.

The legs of the bed were of gold enamel work. I couldn't begin to estimate the value of the coverlets, nor of the candles, nor of the chandeliers which remained burning night and day. They would be worth the total value of an entire city.

As soon as the lady entered this room, her knight recognized her. She ran across to him. She was shivering with fear. She fell in a faint upon his body. He who loved her so dearly opened his arms to her. He pitied her and himself. When she had recovered enough to be able to listen, he comforted her gently.

"Sweet love, I beg you in God's name to go away from here. Run away from here! Escape! I shall die in any case towards midday. Your grief will be so sharp from that, if you are here at the time, that you will be too greatly tortured by it. By then it will become known among my people that they have lost me because of your love. Therefore I am worried and tormented now for your sake!"

"Love," the lady told him, "I much prefer to die here beside you than to go home and suffer pains at the hand of my husband. If I go home to him, he will kill me anyway."

The knight assured her that this would not happen. He gave her a little ring, telling her and lessoning her that as long as she kept the ring on her finger her husband would never once refer to what had occurred and that he would not punish her because of it. Then he commended his sword and gave it into her keeping. He warned her that no man should ever touch it. He forbade her strictly to let anyone but his own son have it. He said she was to guard it closely until his son was old enough to use it.

The dying knight said that when their son had reached his full height and had become a man and when he in his turn had become a brave and valiant knight, that she and her husband were to take the boy to a great feast. There they would enter an abbey where they would see a tomb. There they would hear the story of his death and how he was betrayed and slaughtered. In that abbey she would give their son his father's sword. There the whole adventure would be revealed to the boy: how he was born, who had engendered him. Then they would see what the boy would do.

After the knight had finished instructing the lady, he gave her a beautiful, embroidered robe. He ordered her to dress in it. Then he told her to leave him without delay.

The lady reluctantly left the palace. She wore her lover's ring and carried his sword, which gave her great assurance. She had not left the city more than a half league behind her when she heard bells ringing. Cries of lamentation rose from the walls of the city. The death knell began to toll for the lord of the castle who was just then dying. The lady felt when he was dead. Her pain grew so fierce that four times she fell fainting as she re-crossed the meadow. Each time, as she recovered, she kept walking forward. Finally, she came to the entrance of the hill.

Into the dark tunnel she stumbled, passed through it safely, and found herself back in her own homeland again. . . . Together with her lord she lived many a day and many a week. He never referred to the events of that sad day, never accused her, never chattered about it once.

The lady's child was born. It was a son. He was born easily, and he took food readily. He was well nursed, well reared, and well loved. They named him Yonec.

In all the kingdom could not be found a youth so handsome, so brave, nor so valiant. Neither one so generous nor so unselfish. When he came of age, he was dubbed knight. Now hear what happened in the very year when this took place!

At the feast of Saint Aaron which they were celebrating at Caerleon as well as in several other cities, the lord had been summoned to attend. He therefore decided to go along with several of his friends. He took his wife and her son. She arrayed herself splendidly. They sallied forth and traveled away from their castle. After a while they began to realize that they no longer knew where they were going. They had taken a lad with them as their guide. He led them such a straight route that they eventually came to a castle. In all the century they had never seen one so magnificent.

Inside this castle was an abbey full of monks and nuns. Their valets invited the travelers to dismount. They led away their horses. Other valets showed them to the feast. In the abbot's great hall they were deferentially served and much honored. Next morning they went to hear mass. After this they planned to continue their journey. The abbot, however, said he would like to speak to them. He begged them to remain a little longer. He showed them his dormitories, his chapter rooms, and his refectory. Then he explained to milord how the abbey was administered.

After dinner the abbot continued to take them on another tour of his establishment. He showed them the workrooms next. Then he led the way into the chapter house. There they saw a huge tomb draped with a mantle encrusted with gold. At the head of the sarcophagus were twenty lighted tapers and also twenty more on each of the other sides. The chandelier was of pure gold. The censers were of amethyst. Incense was burned there ever day in order to do perpetual homage at this tomb.

The abbott was asked and asked by all the people in that country whose tomb it was and what man lay there in death. When asked this day, the abbot burst into tears. As he wept he began to tell them the story:

"There was once the best knight in the world, the very bravest and the proudest, the most splendid and the best beloved that any century ever saw. He was, even he, the king of this very land. Never was there one so courteous. He was one morning unexpectedly set upon at Caervent, all through the love of a lady. For her was he slain. Since that day we have been without a prince. We have waited many a day for the son he engendered—for his son and the lady's. This is the son the lady bore just as our prince commanded her to do."

When the lady heard this news, she called her son aloud. "Sweet son," she said, "you have heard how God has brought us here! It is your father who lies here before you and whom that old man cruelly killed. Now I commend to you and so do render unto you your father's sword. I have guarded it long enough."

When she heard all that was told her son, how he was engendered, and whose son he was, how his father used to come to her, and how he had been betrayed, the lady fell fainting on her lover's tomb. She simply wandered out of her life. She never spoke another word.

Her son saw that his lady mother was dead. With his father's sword he cut off the old man's head. Thus the sword which had belonged to the prince took revenge for him and for the lady.

As soon as this happened, these events were quickly known through the city. The lady's body was lifted, placed, and sealed inside the sarcophagus beside the body of her love. May God have mercy on them!

Yonec became the lord of the city. . . . Those who heard this adventure long afterwards made it into a lay which told of the pain and sorrow they suffered for love.

VI

THE ROMANCE OF TRISTRAN

Beroul

TWELFTH CENTURY

Y LORDS, you have certainly heard how Tristran escaped from King Mark's castle by going straight down the rock escarpments and how his squire Governal, (mounted on the war horse), issued forth after him, for he feared lest he be burned at the stake if Mark captured him. Therefore, the lovers are together in the forest where Tristran feeds them on venison. They are under the deep shadows of the trees for a long time, where they find shelter at night and from which they depart every morning.

One day as they wandered, they came to the hermitage of Brother Ogrins. They lead such a harsh and hard life. Tristran and Yseut are so much in love with each other, with such a good love that each one feels the other's pain.

The hermit recognized Tristran. Leaning on his crutch he addressed him, and hear how he spoke: "Sir Tristran, there has been sworn throughout Cornwall a great oath that whoever should turn you in to the king would without fail receive a hundred marks as a reward. There is in this land not a baron who has not sworn upon his lord's hands to surrender you to him, either dead or alive." Then Ogrins added in a kindly fashion: "Upon my soul, Tristran, if a man repents him of his sins, God grants him a pardon if the transgressor has kept the faith and made confession of them."

Tristran said to him: "Sir, on my faith, you must know that she loves me in all truth. You do not understand the workings of this love. That she loves me, comes from the potion. I can no more leave her than she can leave me, and that is the gospel truth."

Ogrins said to him: "And what comfort can one give a dead man? He is virtually dead who wallows long in sin, unless he repents. I cannot give you penance, not to unrepentant sinners." The hermit Ogrins delivered them a long sermon, giving them counsel as to their necessity of repenting. The hermit many times referred to the prophecies of the Holy Writ, reminding them at length and frequently of their errors. In great anxiety of mind he asked Tristran: "What will you do? . . . Be advised."

"Sir, I love Yseut marvelously much, so much so that I neither sleep nor slumber. My advisement has been made from forever. I should prefer to be a beggar as I now am and live upon grasses and acorns than possess the wealth of a Saracen kingdom. Do not ask me to speak of leaving her, for do that I can not."

Yseut weeps at the hermit's feet and keeps asking him for his indulgence: "Sir, by Almighty God, he does not love me and I do not love him except because of that brew that I drank and he drank. There was our sin. For this has the king driven us out of his castle."

The hermit replies at once: "Heavens! the very God who made the world accords you the power of true repentance." And know for sure, without a doubt, that they spent that night in the hermitage. He relaxed his holy rule in order to shelter them.

Early the next morning Tristran sets out. He avoids open fields and keeps to the dark trees. They need bread to eat, which is a sore necessity. Of stags, of fawns, of kids he can kill enough in the forest. There, wherever they find shelter for the night, they do their cooking and build up their bright fire. Only one night do they stay in any one place.

Lords, hear how against Tristran the king has had his bans cried. There is not anywhere in Cornwall a parish where this does not cause anguish. The king promises that whoever knows the whereabouts of Tristran should raise a hue and cry.

Let him who cares to hear this adventure where there is great value in the lesson it tells, let him listen to me for a little bit. You will hear me tell of a splendid hunting dog, the like of which no count or king ever owned. He was a beautiful dog, swift and not sluggish, and so he was called Hudent. He was tied to a stake. The dogs were kept in the keep; especially well tied was Hudent, for he had become very upset when he no longer saw his master near him. He would no longer eat either bread or any food, not even a morsel that was stretched out to him. He growled and pawed and tears flowed from his eyes. God! How sorry everybody was for that dog! People said: "If that were my animal, I would untie him from the clog; for if he goes mad, it will be such a pity. Ah! Hudent! Never will another hunter like you be found, so ready to run, so mournful because of your master. There never was a dog so fond of a human being. . . . Solomon says quite aptly that one's best friends are one's greyhounds. We can prove it by you. Hudent, because you won't touch a morsel and haven't eaten since your master was seized. King, let the dog loose!"

The king had considered the matter. He knew the dog was raging because he had lost his master. "Certainly, the dog has great good sense. I don't believe that in our time, in all the land of Cornwall, there is a single knight who can be compared to Tristran."

Three barons from Cornwall reasoned with the king. "Sire, do untie Hudent. Then we will know for sure if the dog is suffering because of his master's misfortune. For if you don't let him loose soon and if he bites someone, then maybe he's enraged and he will hurt something or some animal or some person. Let him loose. Then see his tongue hanging out into the wind."

The king called a squire to untie Hudent. The servants stood on benches and saddles for they feared the dog's first free lunge. They all said, "Hudent is mad." The dog had no intention of attacking them. As soon as he was freed, he ran alert through the files of people so fast that he was like a streak. He went out the front door of the hall straight to the lodging where he used to find Tristran. The king saw him and so did the others who came behind him.

The dog yelped and growled often. He whined as if he were in pain. He sniffed along the road after Tristran. Never did his master take a step from the time he was seized to the place where he was to have been burned at the stake that the dog did not take after him. Hudent runs into the chamber where Tristran was betrayed and seized, and leaves, jumps out, gives tongue in a clear bark, and goes yelping towards the chapel. Folks run through the streets after the dog. Then since Tristran did not die after he was out of his bonds, the dog leaped up to the minster that was perched on the cliff. The lively dog could not see inside the church so he ran inside, jumped on the altar, didn't see his master, then leaped out a window and landed

121

on the cliff where he hurt his leg. He was up immediately, nose to the ground, baying.

Hudent halted briefly at the edge of the flowering wood where Tristran had set the ambush, then started forth again, straight into the forest. Not a soul saw this happen but felt pity for the animal. The knights told the king: "Let the dog trail him unmolested. He could lead us into such a spot as we would be in dire straits for the return." They left the dog and returned.

The dog leaped across a clearing in the trees, joyous at having been set free on an open road. The whole woods echoed with his baying. Tristran was deeper in the woods with the queen and Governal. They heard the racket. Tristran listened. "On my life," he cried, "I hear Hudent." They were afraid and very frightened. Tristran leaped up and stretched his bow. They were all ready to take flight farther into the woods. There is the king's price on their heads, and so they were dismayed, thinking he came with the dog.

Hudent was not long in coming, for he smelled out the right path easily. When he caught sight of his master and knew him, then he tossed his head and wagged his tail. Whoever could have seen him wriggling with joy would have said he never saw such a happy dog. He ran up to Yseut of the blond hair and then to Governal. He greeted them all, even the horse.

Tristran felt great pity for the dog. "Oh, God!" he said, "by what bad luck did that animal get to find us? A dog which doesn't know how to be still in the forest has no business near a tracked man. We are here hated by the king and in his woods. King Mark has sent out a search for us, Lady, through plains, and woods, and the whole earth. If he were able to find us and take us, he would have us burned or hanged. We have no business with a dog. You may as well know that if Hudent remains with us, he will cause us all kinds of calamities. It is probably better that he be killed than for us to be captured because of his baying. It makes me very sad, since he is such a loyal dog, to think that he came here on the track of death.

"It was his nature that instructed him, but how can I solve this difficulty otherwise? For sure, it grieves me sorely to think that I shall have to kill him. So give me your advice. What can we do with this dog?"

Yseut told him: "Sire, take pity on him. The dog hunts with his tongue, according to his nature and his training. I once heard tell that a certain man had a Welsh forester—since Arthur was crowned king—who had so trained a dog that when he hunted a stag he only followed the spoor and had been taught to do it silently, without giving tongue. Friend Tristran, it would be wonderful if you could take the pains to make Hudent stop making a noise—if you could teach him to hunt and be silent."

Tristran was silent as he listened. He was so sorry for his dog. He thought for a while before replying. Then he said that he would try her suggestion. Within a month the dog was dressed. He became very useful to them, for he hunted every day for their food.

> *Seignors, molt fu el bois Tristrans,*
> *Molt i out paines et ahans.*
> *En un leu n'ose remanoir;*
> *Dont lieve au matin ne gist au soir ...*

Lords, for a long time Tristran was in the wood where he had much pain and exhaustion. He did not dare remain in any place. He never lay down at night in the spot where he had arisen that morning. He knew that the king was searching for him and that bans had been cried throughout the land for him to be taken if anyone could find him. While they hid in the woods, they were distressed by the lack of bread. They lived only on flesh with nothing else to eat. Their clothes became ripped by twigs and branches.

123

For a long time they fled through the forest of Morrois. Each one of them suffered an equal pain, for each felt the ills of the other.

The gentle Yseut was very much afraid that Tristran would regret what he had done, and Tristran for his part worried for fear she would stop loving him and would repent of her folly.

Lords, it was a summer's day at that time, as in the month of August, after Pentecost. In the morning when the birds were singing sun-up in the dew, Tristran arose from the shelter where he had slept, buckled on his sword, went out alone to hunt with his marvelous Unfailing Arc. Were there ever people in such trouble? Each one felt for the other, and so they were happy together. Ever since the forest had been created, there had not been such lovers as they were. Nor did ever, as says the story which Béroul read, had any people so loved each other as they loved, nor so grievously, nor so dearly.

As soon as Tristran returned, the queen ran up to him. The day was so hot that they were heavy and slow. Tristran hugged her to him and she said: . . .

"Friend, where have you been?"

"After a stag that escaped from me. I followed him so far that I am weary. Sleep has come over me. I want to lie down and rest." Their bower was made of green branches stretched across each other so that the sunlight pierced the leaves and fell in yellow patches on their carpet of green. Yseut lay down first. Then Tristran lay down, drew his sword, and put it between his flesh and hers. Yseut kept on her chemise—if she had been naked that day, marvelous mischief would have been done—and Tristran wore his trews.

On her finger the queen wore the golden wedding ring she had from the king. It was set with emeralds. Her finger had grown so very thin that it was a marvel the ring did not fall from her hand. Hear how they lay: Tristran had put his arm under her shoulders, and the other arm—it seems to me—he had thrown over her. He held her tightly and he sang to her clasped in his arms. . . . Their love was a real love—and no pretense.

Their lips were almost touching, and yet they had so managed it that they were not resting against each other. The wind didn't ripple; no leaf trembled; a ray of sunlight fell on Yseut's face which gleamed like a mirror. Thus the lovers slept together and meant no harm, neither how much nor so much. In all that place they were alone to each other, for Governal—as it seems to me—had taken the horse and gone off deeper into the forest.

Now hear, lords, the adventure that befell them. It was so bitter and so harsh! Through the forest came a woodsman who had found the bower where they lay. He knew the secret paths so well that he had stolen under the boughs to the very place where Tristran had cut branches for their shelter. He saw them asleep, recognized them. His blood stopped; so amazed was he. He crept away softly, for well he suspected—rather knew it for certain—that if Tristran awoke he would not take him as hostage except for his head which he would take as first payment. That the woodsman ran is no marvel. He ran full speed until he was out of the forest.

Tristran slept with his love, not knowing that he had just narrowly escaped death. From the place where they slept, it was about two good leagues to the king's court. The forester ran straight there, for he had heard of the price on Tristran's head. He knew that the man who indicated his whereabouts would be well rewarded.

King Mark was in his palace hearing pleas. The hall was full of his barons. The woodsman climbed the steps and burst into the room. Do you think he was stopped before he came to the throne room? No. . . . The king saw him rush in all out of breath. "Let's hear your news," said the king. "You look like a man running to hounds. Have you come to court with a complaint? You look like a man who is in dire need. I feel it from here. If you like, speak your piece. Have they not paid your wages? Have they driven you out of my preserve?"

"Listen to me, King, if you please, and see if you understand. From this country they published that if anyone could locate your nephew, rather than let himself get killed or taken, he should come and say so. I found him and I fear your wrath. If I tell you, will I be killed? I can take you where he sleeps and the queen with him. I saw him just a while ago, if I am right. They were sound asleep. I was very frightened when I saw them."

The king, puffing and sighing, listened to the man. He was upset and very angry. He whispered to the woodsman, "In what place are they? Tell me."

"In a lodge in Morrois. They are asleep tight and folded in each other's arms. Come quickly and we will be avenged. King, if you can't take a sharp revenge for this, then there is unmistakably no justice on the earth."

The king told him, "Go outside here. Act as if you were going on a trip. Don't say a word about this to anyone, no matter how they approach you. Go to the fork in the road at the Red Cross where the hunt often assembles. Don't move from there. Wait for me. I'll give you all the gold and silver you want."

The woodsman left the king, went to the Cross, sat down and waited. May he go blind for wanting to destroy Tristran! . . . He would have done better to mind his hunting, for he died a shameful death as you shall hear in the story.

Meanwhile, the king returned to his courtroom where he instructed all his courtiers not to so much dare as to follow him. Each one said, "King, is it right for you to go somewhere alone? No self-respecting king ever did such a thing. What news have you heard? Don't take action on what some spy said."

"No news," the king replied. "A maiden requested me to come and speak with her. She asked me not to bring attendants. I'll go alone on my horse, taking neither peer nor squire. This time I'll go without you."

They answered, "This disturbs us. Cato instructed his son to eschew solitary places."

"I know that," he said. "For once let me have my way."

The king had his horse saddled, his sword buckled, all the while cursing the stealth which Tristran had used when he kidnaped Yseut of the fair face, with whom he went fleeing. If he found them, he knew what punishment he would use. He would not let them escape this time. The king thirsted for blood, which is a great sin. He rode out of the city. It would be better to die on the gallows, he thought, than not to be revenged for the wrong they did him. He came to the Cross where the man waited, told him to hurry it up, and take a straight road.

They plunged into the woods. The shade was deep. The king had the scout precede him. He followed, trusting in the good sword he had buckled to his belt, for it had beheaded many. His confidence was not misplaced, for if Tristran awoke, so that uncle and nephew could meet, one of them would die before it was settled. He told the forester he would give him twenty marks if he led him straight to the crime. The abashed woodsman replied that they were nearing the end of their toil. He helped the king dismount from his big Gascon horse. Then he tied the animal to an apple tree bough. They crept forward until they were in sight of the bower.

127

The king untied his cloak with its tassels of pure gold. When he tossed it aside, he stood there ready. He had a handsome body. He drew his sword from its scabbard, muttering under his breath that he wished to die if he did not slay them. Holding his naked sword before him, he entered the bower. The forester followed, entering quickly on the king's heels. The king motioned him back. Then the king raised the sword above his head. He was angry, so angry he felt faint. The blade was already on its way down. It would have cut them in two—such a pity—when the king saw that she had on her chemise which separated the two, that their lips were close but not touching, when he saw the naked sword which lay full and shining between them, when he saw Tristran clad in his breeches.

"God," said the king, "what does this mean? Now have I seen so much of their selves and yet I do not know what I should do, whether to kill them or to withdraw. Here they are, right here in this wood, where they have been for such a long time. If I have any wit at all, I can see that they are madly in love. If they had no clothing between them and no drawn sword, if they were otherwise together, then I would have had the courage to slaughter them.

"I shall not touch them. I shall go away with my wrath. They have not the intent to consummate their wild love ("*fole amour*"). I shall do nothing. They sleep. If they were touched by me as they sleep, I would bring too great a sin upon myself. And were I to awaken this sleeping knight and were he to kill me or I him, the retelling of it would either way be hideous.

"I will leave them a sign to show them, before they awaken, so that they will know for certain that I found them here asleep and that I took pity on them, that I no way desired to kill them, neither I nor the nobles of my empire. . . . On the queen's finger I see the wedding band with its emeralds that once I gave her. It is a lovely ring.

And I will then again have a ring which was hers. I will slip off my ring from her finger.

"With me I have my fur-trimmed gauntlets which she brought me when she came as my bride from Ireland. With them I will shut out this ray of sunlight which streaks across her face. She will suffer from such heat on her skin. And then as I leave I will take his sword which lies drawn between them. It was the sword he won from Morhot in Ireland."

The king unfastened his gauntlets. Still looking down at the sleeping pair, he placed the gloves so that they would shade the queen's face. Then he slipped the gold band from her finger. She did not even stir; he touched her so softly. Her finger had grown so thin that the ring slid off easily. Then ever so gently he drew the sword from between them, putting his own in its place. Then he tiptoed away from the bower, leaped on his horse and started home. He told the forester to hide in a hurry, to be gone.

The king thus departed, leaving them asleep. For that time he did no more. He returned to his city. When people on all sides asked him where he went and was, he lied to them, and they never knew where he had gone nor what he had sought nor of any doing he had done.

But now hear about those sleepers whom the king had abandoned in the wood. It seemed to the queen that she was in a vast woodland and inside a rich pavilion. Two lions came up to her. They were going to devour her. She wanted to beg them for mercy, but the lions, distressed by famine, took her hands in their mouths. From terror Yseut screamed and awoke just as the gauntlets, trimmed with white ermine, fell on her breast.

She awoke Tristran with her cry. He saw that her face was flushed crimson. He was so frightened that he leaped to his feet, reaching like a desperate man for his sword. He stared at the blade. It was not his. He saw its golden hilt and recognized it as the king's sword. . . . The queen looked at her finger. Her ring was gone. In its place was the king's ring.

"Sir, look," she cried. "The king found us here."

"Lady, that is true," he answered. "Now we must decamp from Morrois, for we are discovered. He has replaced my sword with his. He could have slain us."

"Sir, true, I think so, too."

"Beauty, all we can do is flee. He left us here to betray us at leisure. . . . He was alone. . . . He must have gone for his attendants. Truly, he will be back to seize us.

"Lady, let us flee into Wales. My blood runs cold."

They were afraid. There was no other course open to them but flight. They knew the king was envious and treacherous. Therefore they set out as fast as they could journey, for fear of the king's next move. They crossed Morrois forest and left it behind them. They traveled each day all day long. They headed straight for Wales. Their love had caused them all these hardships. For three long, full years they suffered the pains of love. Their skins grew pale. Their bodies grew gaunt.

Lords, you have heard of the wine they drank which caused them to be set so long in pain. But you do not yet know, it seems to me, how this love drink was brewed, how this wine was steeped. It was Yseut's mother who boiled it for three years out of kindness. She prepared it for Mark and for her daughter. Let someone else prove otherwise, if he thinks he can. So long as the three years lasted, this wine had so taken Tristran and the queen out of their senses that then they said: "Honor is fled."

The morning after Saint John's day the three years of the wine's domination were ended. Tristran rose from his bed, leaving Yseut on her couch of leaves. All that day Tristran tracked a stag he had wounded. Up hill and down dale he rode until the hour came. He stopped. It was the exact moment when he had drunk the love drink. Then all to himself he began to repent: "Oh, God, what travail have I known! It is three years today. I have forgotten chivalry, the court, my baronage. I am an exile from my native land without robes or furs, without a court, without knights. God! How dearly my uncle loved me! If I only had not committed such a misdeed! How weak I was!

"God, Lord of the world, give me the courage to leave my uncle's wife in peace. I vow to God that I will do it most willingly, if I can, so that Yseut may be reconciled to King Mark whom she wedded."

Now hear how Yseut was: "Alas, wretched queen, how happy you once were! You live in a wood now like a serving girl. I am a queen, but I lost my name because of the poison we drank at sea. It was Brengain's fault. She was supposed to guard it. She watched it very ill, indeed! Damsels of honor, daughters of great vavasors should be my companions in my chamber, to serve me. And I should be arranging their marriages to lords of high estate.

"Friend Tristran, through a terrible mistake we drank the love brew together."

"Gentle queen," said Tristran, "we are wasting our youth. Dear friend, if only I could find a way to reconcile you to King Mark so that he forgave our misconduct and never once accused you, and if he were only ready to believe that I was never your lover; for if he wished to say that my love for you was dishonorable, he would have to meet me armed on the field; but if he wanted to admit me again to his household, I would serve him in all honor as my uncle and my liege lord. And if it were his pleasure to take you

131

and banish me, if he had no care for my services, I would go to the Frisian king, or I would cross over into Brittany with Governal and no other companion."

Together they went to ask the hermit's advice. They found Ogrins in his cell reading. When he saw them, he spoke roundly: "Oh, the outcasts! With what great pain does Love lead you astray! You have led this life too long. Tell me, pray, why you do not repent."

Tristran answered: "Now listen. We have led it too long; such was 'our destiny. For three full years, unless I am mistaken, and never yet eased our suffering. If we can find a way to have the queen reinstated, I will go away into Brittany, or into Lyonesse. If my uncle will endure my presence at his court, I will serve him as I am in duty bound to do. Sir, my uncle is a powerful man, . . ."

Lords, hear how the queen knelt with bowed head at the hermit's feet, begging him to reconcile her to her lord: "I shall never have again any day of my life the courage of my own folly. I do not say in your intention that I am sorry I love Tristran with true love and as my friend without any dishonor or intimate knowledge of my body, or I of his."

When the hermit heard her words, tears came to his eyes because he was all in adoration before God. "Oh, God, omnipotent and lovely King, grace; for my heart breaks to think that You have let me live to see the day when these two leave off their sins and come to me for counsel. Great is the grace I can render unto You. . . . I swear that you will have good counsel from me.

"When a man and a woman have sinned, if they mend their ways and do penance, and repent them sincerely, God pardons their misdeed, no matter how horrible and how ugly."

Although Tristran repeated constantly that no one could trust King Mark's word, no matter how solemnly given, the hermit drew up a series of propositions to which King Mark acceded—that he would receive his queen and return her to her former state of honor and magnificence, and that, since he did not wish to keep Tristran near him or at his court, he would allow his nephew to depart safely into exile. Tristran was to choose a place where war was being fought. After a year or two he could then sue King Mark for leave to return.

"God," said Tristran, "what a way to part! A man is so sad when he loses his love. It must be done, however, for the suffering you have borne for my sake. When we come to the instant of our parting, I will pledge you my everlasting love, and you yours to me, dear friend. I shall not be in that land where I may have peace or war without sending you word of me. Sweet love, from time to time let me have news of your pleasure."

With a deep sigh Yseut spoke: "Tristran, hear me a little. Leave me your dog Hudent. No hunting dog shall ever be so well tended by any hunter as he will be tended by me, dear and sweet friend. Whenever I see him I know that then I shall be remembering you. Whenever my heart is heavy and I see Hudent, then I will be glad again. Never since the earth was ordained shall any animal have been so lodged or given such a soft bed.

"My friend, Tristran, I have a little ring, with a stone of green jasper in the seal. Good Sir, wear this ring on your finger out of love for me. And if it ever comes to your mind that you send me a message, I will say and know it well, most certainly, that I won't believe it comes from you unless I see the ring. But, notwithstanding the orders of any king whoever he may be, I will not stop from doing anything you tell me to do, whether it be a wisdom or a folly, so long as it is consistent with our honor.

"Friend, will you give me such a rare gift as your dog Hudent?"

And he answered, "My own dear friend, I will give you Hudent out of my true love."

"Sir, you show pity on me by giving me your dog. Take this ring as your guerdon." Then they kissed and parted.

The hermit went to Saint Michael's Mount where he purchased all sorts of rich apparel for the lovers: furs, silk cloth and purple, scarlet linen and white as pure as the lily, and a softly ambling palfrey well caparisoned and studded with gold. The hermit Ogrins bought so much and bartered so much and bargained so well that finally the queen was richly provided. She was to meet the king at the Adventurous Ford. . . . I have heard it from hearsay myself that there was neither a knight nor a damsel who did not witness this meeting. The queen was very popular and deeply loved by all, except by felons whom God destroy! And, indeed, God did crush four who had tried to bring low her proud estate.

On the day established for this conference, King Mark brought countless attendants. There were pitched scores of pavilions, scores of barons' tents which from afar off crimsoned the meadow.

Tristran came riding alongside his friend . . . up to the boundary stone. He wore his hauberk under his gown. He was afraid for his life, knowing full well how he had wronged the king. He scanned the tents scattered over the field and recognized those of the king and his assembly.

"Lady Yseut," said Tristran, "keep Hudent close to you. I beg you for God's sake to hold on to him. If you ever loved that dog, then love him now. I see the king, your lord, and with him many men of high rank. We cannot go along talking together much longer. I see the knights, and the king, and his foot soldiers already coming towards us. If I tell you to do something hastily or with emphasis, Lady, be sure to do it."

"Friend Tristran, listen to me. By this faith I owe you,

if you do not send me the ring you now wear on your finger, if I do not see it, I won't believe anything anyone says. But as soon as I see the ring, neither tower nor stronghold, nor rampart will sway me from doing the will of my love, if only it is honorable and loyal and I know it is your pleasure."

"Lady," he said, "may God show his mercy upon you." Then he drew her to him and enfolded her in his arms.

Yseut, who was very well spoken, said: "Friend, listen to my words. I want you to understand my thinking. You are now taking me and wish to return me to the king according to the advice of the hermit Ogrins. May he make a good end! In the name of God, I beg you, sweet friend, not to depart from this land until you know whether the king is wrathful towards me or forgiving."

The king did not wish Tristran to remain, however, and this was the opinion of his barons also. When he knew the king's pleasure, Tristran and the queen took leave of each other. The queen blushed, for she was ashamed in front of the assembly. She and Tristran looked once more at each other, straight in the eyes. Then Tristran turned away and rode from the assembly. He rode towards the seacoast. Yseut accompanied him with her eyes. As long as he was in sight, she did not move.

VII

EREC AND ENIDE

Chrétien de Troyes

TWELFTH CENTURY

NE MORNING when they were in bed and having great delight, lying mouth to mouth in each other's arms like those who are very much in love, it happened. He was asleep, but she was awake. At that moment she remembered the words which were being said about her lord by many people in the country. As she lay recalling them, she could not help but weep. She was so sad and heavy that accidentally she spoke aloud —a thing she later called herself a fool for having done. At the moment she intended no mischief.

She raised her head and began to stare at her lord who lay there with his shapely body and handsome face. She draped herself across his chest again and, weeping hot tears all over him, began to say, "Alas, how unlucky for me that I ever left my own country! What did I come here for any-

137

way? It would have been better for the earth to have swallowed me up than for the best knight, the most daring and the proudest, the handsomest and the most courteous, more even than count or king, to have relinquished his chivalry because of me. Thus have I dishonored him for sure, a thing I should not have wished to do for anything."

Before she fell silent, Enide said with a great sigh, "You came to me for your misfortune!"

Erec was not very fast asleep. He half heard her last words, which awoke him completely. He was amazed to see her weeping so violently. He therefore questioned her. "Tell me, dear love, why do you weep in this way? Why are you upset and sad? Certainly, I want to know this. Tell me, dear love, and watch out not to try to conceal it from me. Why did you say that I went to you for my misfortune? You said that for my ears and for no others. I heard your words perfectly well."

Then was Enide distressed. She was not only dismayed. She was afraid. "Sire," she said, "I don't know what you are talking about."

"Lady, why are you trying to deny it? You can't hide it, you know. You have been crying, and I can see it. You never cried about anything before. Even as I slept, I heard what you said."

"Oh, dear Sire, you didn't hear it at all. And anyway, I think I must have been dreaming."

"Now you are concocting lies for me. Now you are lying openly. You will regret it later, I promise you, if you don't own up to the truth now!"

"Sire, even though you are distressing me, I will tell you the truth. I will not hide it any longer, but I am very much afraid you won't like it. . . . All over the country, everybody—the black-haired and the blonds and the red-heads—everybody is saying that it is too bad of you to have abandoned your arms. They say that now you are

138

worth much less. A year ago they used to say that there wasn't a better or more valiant knight in all the world, that you had nowhere your equal. Now they go around gabbing about you—old and young, little and big. All call you a coward.

"Don't you think it hurts me when I hear them scorn you? It hangs heavily upon me every time I hear them say such things. And what hurts me even more is that they blame it on me. That really hurts. They say that is the reason why you have forsaken chivalry and lost all your value and don't even want to hear about it. It is better for you to take a new resolution in order to quench such censure and attain again your former glory. I have heard you reviled too often, and I never dared tell you before. Very often, whenever I remembered it, I have wept. Today I felt so wretched about it that I forgot to be on my guard, and so the words escaped me."

"Lady," he said, "that was your right. And those who censured me were right. Now go get dressed immediately and prepare to ride. Get out of bed and dress in your finest gown and have your best palfrey saddled for the road."

Then Enide was even more frightened. Sad and pensive, she arose from the bed. She scolded herself and blamed herself alone for the foolish words she had said. The goat scratches around so much that he ruins his bed. "Oh," she told herself, "you stupid fool! Then I was too comfortable —so cozy, in fact, that I lacked nothing. God! Why was I so forward as to dare say such nonsense? God! Did not milord love me too much? On my word, alas, he did that! Now I have to go into exile! Even more sorrowful than that is the fact that I won't see my husband, Erec, who loved me so much in such a grand manner that nothing was too expensive for me. The best man ever born was so wrapped up in me that he paid no attention to anything else. I lacked for nothing. I was so fortunate.

"My pride caused me to rise up and say such a great outrage to him. It is only right that I be punished. Nobody knows what good is until he has tried the bad."

As she thought, the lady went about having herself attired in the best dress she had; but nothing pleased her, so troubled were her thoughts. When she was almost ready, she sent word by one of her maidens that her rich Norwegian palfrey be saddled. No count or king had a finer horse. Her orders were obeyed at once.

Without any explanation, Erec called his valets and told them to fetch his armor and then to arm him for combat. Then he climbed up to one of his loges where a Limoges carpet was spread on the tile floor. Sitting there, Erec had his accoutrements brought. First they put on his cuisses and kneepieces of white steel and tied them. After that they slipped on his hauberk of chain mail so finely linked that no one could break it. This hauberk was so intricately woven before and behind that no piece of steel the size of a needle could pierce it. The whole was of silver reinforced with tiny links of steel mesh. It was so cunningly worked that I can certainly tell you that he who wore it was no more weary than as if he had drawn on over his shirt a suit of sheer silk.

The castle sergeants and the knights were all completely mystified as to why Sir Erec was having himself armed, but none of them dared ask him. After his hauberk had been fastened, his helmet with a circle of gold on it, more polished than a mirror, was set on his head and laced above his gorget. Then he took his sword and slipped it on his belt. Then he called for his bay horse from Gascony to be saddled. He told a valet, "Go at once. Run to the chamber near the tower where milady is. Tell her that she is keeping me waiting too long here. She has spent too much time getting dressed! Tell her to come up here at once, for I am waiting."

When the valet arrived in her chamber, he found the lady in tears, bemoaning her plight. The servant said, "Lady! why do you delay so long? Milord is out there awaiting you. He is all armed. He would have been on horseback long ago if you had been ready."

Enide couldn't imagine what her lord husband had in mind. She decided it would be better for her if she could contain her emotion when she appeared before him. By the time she presented herself, the whole court was there. King Lac had just come running into his son's presence. Knights were dashing about. Not a single oldster or youngster but wanted to know and to ask if the lord did not want him to go along. Everyone more than offered his services. Everyone insisted.

Erec swore that he would take no companion with him except his wife—and none other. It was as sure as sure that otherwise he would go alone. At this news the king was most distressed. "Good son," he cried, "what are you going to do? To me at least you ought to explain your affair. You ought not to hide anything from me! Tell me where you are wanting to go. You really do not want any squires and knights to make up your escort? If you have undertaken a single combat with a knight, even so you ought not to refuse an escort. You ought to have a party with you, for prestige, because of your position. A king's son should not go alone. Good son, have your pack mules loaded and take thirty or forty knights, or oven more than that that. Also have some gold and silver about you, as befits a nobleman."

"Sire," replied Erec, "it cannot be otherwise. I shall take no horses or war steeds with me. I have no use for gold or silver, or for sergeant or squire. I require no company save that of my wife alone. However, I do beg of you that whatever happens, if I die and she returns, that you love her and cherish her for the love of me and because of my prowess, and that you settle upon her the half of your lands promptly, without suits or wars, and this bequest for her lifetime."

"Good son, I so grant. But of your going forth in this wise, without any companions, I am greatly grieved. You would not have done such a thing with my consent."

"Sire, it cannot be otherwise. Commending you to God, I now take my leave. Think still of my old companions, I pray. See that they have horses and arms as a knight must." The king could not keep from weeping when he saw his son depart. On all sides people were crying. Ladies and knights wept and carried on very sadly. Not a single one but was so affected. Many fell fainting there in the courtyard as they kissed him and hugged him. They almost went insane from grief. They probably could not have mourned more deeply if they had suddenly seen him already dead or wounded.

Erec spoke to them as comforting words as he knew how to do. "Lord father, why do you weep so loudly? I am neither seized nor crippled. And as I now go away, I shall return when God wills and I can. I commend you one and all to God's care. Therefore say farewell. You are causing me to delay too long. When I see you weep and cry, I am touched and saddened."

Thus they departed amidst great lamentation. Erec left home taking his wife with him. He didn't know where he was bound—just for adventure.

"Let's go," he told Enide, "and top speed. And watch yourself. Do not dare, no matter what you see before you, to speak a word to me ever! So be careful. Don't say a single word unless I speak to you first. Go forward at a good clip. Ride!"

"Sire," she replied. "Good luck."

Enide led the way, therefore, and rode smartly. Neither one nor the other said another word. Enide was very sad. She complained to herself, but very softly so he wouldn't

143

hear her. "Alas," she murmured, "to think that God set me up and raised me so high and then so shortly after cast me so low! Fortune, which had stretched out her hand, as quickly retracted it. Even at that I wouldn't care at all if I could only talk to my husband. But now I am dead and betrayed since I see he hates me. He hates me all right. I can see that because he won't talk to me. No matter how much I dare otherwise, I just don't dare turn around and look at him."

While Enide was complaining to herself and feeling sorry, a robber knight came out of the forest. There were two others with him. "Say! Do you know what I see?" called the first thief. "If we are not winners today, let us be called clumsy, cowardly, and marvelously unlucky. There comes a very fine lady, lady or damsel, one or the other. She is very richly attired. Her palfrey with the saddle, the harness, and the trappings are worth their weight in gold! I want the palfrey for myself. You can have the rest. That's all I want. God save me, but the knight won't keep anything of the lady's. I'll give him such a rush that he will pay dearly. Since I saw him first, it's my privilege to attack."

Enide saw the robbers. She was very frightened. "God!" she cried. "What can I say? My lord will either be killed or captured. There are three of them, but he is alone. That's not fair play—three against one. They can hit him from behind before he can turn to charge. God! Shall I be so cowardly as not to dare speak? No, I won't be." Turning about, Enide called to her husband. "Good lord," she cried. "What's the matter with you? Three knights are spurring towards you. I am afraid they will hurt you."

"What," cried Erec, "did you say? You have no high opinion of me! You are very brazen, indeed, to have broken my commandment and disobeyed my orders. . . . You shall be forgiven this one time, but if it happens again, then you won't be pardoned."

Then Erec raised his shield, aimed his lance, and spurred

forward against the first assailant. The knight missed, but Erec did not. He split the robber's shield from top to bottom, pierced his hauberk, and drove his lance a foot and a half through his body. As he drew it out again, the robber knight fell to the ground dead. Then the second knight rode away from his companion, took aim, and spurred forward at a gallop. Erec was already more than halfway to him. Their armor shocked. The robbers's lance split in two from the impact. Erec drove his lance a quarter through the second knight's body and left this assailant toppled backwards in his saddle unconscious forever. Before Erec had started for the third knight, that robber had already started galloping back into the forest.

"You vassal!" Erec called after him. "Turn around and fight, or I will run you through the back!" Since the third knight kept going, Erec had to catch him from the rear. He struck him such a blow on the shield that he toppled to the ground. . . . There was nothing more to fear. . . . Erec tied the three war horses together by their bridles and took them to his wife. He told her to drive them ahead of her and not to dare speak to him a second time.

"Just as you please," she answered. They set forth again, and she kept still.

They had not gone more than a league when at the entrance to a valley they saw five knights in front of them. All five were in full armor, their lances in position before them, their shields hung about their necks, and their visors closed. They also were out for spoil. They watched the lady approach, driving the three horses before her and the one knight following. They were already dividing the plunder as if they had finished taking it. They were not used to being crossed. Covetousness has this about it which is bad: only a fool thinks he can get much; even he who is about to fail thinks he can get everything. Thus it happened in this case.

One said he would take the damsel or die in the attempt. One said he would get one of the steeds or nothing. The third wanted the black horse. The fourth, the white horse. The fifth, who was no coward, aimed for the horse and the arms of the knight. Therefore they settled among themselves the order in which they would attack.

Erec saw the first one getting ready, but he pretended that he had not noticed anything. When Enide saw what was before her, her blood stopped. She was terribly frightened. "Alas!" she thought. "I don't know what to say or do! Milord has so threatened me and told me how he will punish me if I speak one more word to him. But if my lord were dead, that would be cold comfort for me. I, too, would be dead and finished. God! My lord hasn't seen them! What am I waiting for, stupid fool that I am? My words cost me dear, those I spoke to him a while ago. I know these knights are robbers. How shall I tell him? He will kill me if I speak. . . . Well, let him, then. I won't let him stop me from speaking."

Then very softly Enide called, "Lord!"

"What," he cried, "do you want to say?"

"Thanks, Sire. I want to say that five knights have just come out of that thicket, and I am afraid. I think they are going to fight you. Four wait behind, but the fifth one is coming now as fast as his horse can carry him. He's going to shock with you in a minute. The four aren't far behind him. They will come to his aid."

Erec replied, "You thought wrong when you disobeyed what I ordered you to do. I already found out some time ago how unworthy you think I am. You are not doing me any good offices now, either. I am not obliged to you. Now I hate you all the more. I told you before, and I will say it again. I will pardon you this time more, but the next time I warn you to be more careful. You would really be a fool to continue your disrespect. I do not like your conversation."

Then the knight closed with Erec. His shield flew into the air. Erec broke his shoulder blade, ripped his stirrups. The assailant fell so hard he never would rise again. Then Erec cut off the second knight's head. He caught the third as he was crossing the stream and drowned both him and his horse. The last two turned in flight. Erec killed the fourth. The last knight threw down his arms and rolled off his horse onto the grass. The combat was finished. Erec took the five horses he had won and joining them to the other three commanded Enide to drive them before her and not to speak to him. She did not reply. Once more they set out on Erec's quest.

They rode until it was very dark without finding either town or refuge. They were finally obliged to spend the night under a tree in the forest. Although Erec volunteered to stand guard, Enide insisted on doing so herself. Therefore, while he slept, she watched through the long hours of the night and blamed herself severely for her overweening pride, but more especially for having doubted her husband's prowess and spirit. In the morning they met a valet who, recognizing them as members of some great and noble line, offered them food and then arranged lodgings for them with a burgess in a neighboring city. Erec rewarded the valet handsomely by presenting him with one of his captured horses. The valet served a proud and wealthy count who, hearing of the strange knight who possessed such an extraordinarily beautiful lady, set out to pay them a visit.

The count took only three companions with him—no more. Erec rose to greet him, for his manners were impeccable. "Sire, be welcome," he said. The count then saluted Erec, and the two sat down side by side on a soft, white cushion. The count offered to be Erec's host. His offer was even urgent. Erec, however, would not accept. He said he was amply provided. As they sat there talking of one thing and another, the count never stopped craning his neck in order to study the lady. He paid only indifferent attention to what he was saying. He looked and looked at Enide until he had decided that she pleased him no end— until, in fact, he had fallen in love with her.

"Sir," he said abruptly to Erec, "I request your leave, and I hope this does not offend you, out of plain courtesy and amiability only, to sit beside the lady. I really came to meet both of you. You must not misinterpret this, for I only desire to present her with my compliments and ask if I can be of service to her. You may rest assured that I shall, out of love for you, become her devoted servant."

Since Erec was not a jealous man, he saw no harm in the count's request. "Sir," he acceded, "I am not in the least offended. Sit down and speak with her as you wish. I don't mind. I willingly grant you leave to do so." The lady sat about two lance lengths away from them. The count sat beside her on a little stool.

"Ah," he cried, "how troubled I am to see you undergoing such ugliness on your journey! I pity you and am disconsolate. If you were ready to rely upon me, you would have every honor and luxury and advantage done you. Great honor and chivalrous service alone are due your beauty. I would make you my love, if you so pleased. You would live well. You would be my cherished sweetheart and the mistress of all my lands. When I condescend to sue for your love, you must not take offense. I know and can see that your lord neither loves nor appreciates you. You would be assorted with a better lord if you chose to remain with me."

"Sir," she replied, "you are wasting your time. This cannot be. It would have been better for me not ever to have been born, or to burn in a fire of thorns and have my ashes scattered than to betray my lord in any way, or even to consider such felony and such treason. You have erred greatly in soliciting such things from me. I shall consider no such offer."

Then the count began to lose his temper. "So, you would

148

not deign to love me, Lady?" he cried. "You are too proud. You would not do what I say either from praise or from prayer? True it is that a woman grows prouder the more a man begs her and praises her! He who mistreats and outrages her often finds her more amenable. I guarantee you all right that if you do not do my will, there will be swords drawn. Right or wrong, I'll have your lord slain right here before your eyes."

"Oh, Sir," said Enide, "you can do better than you say. You would be too treacherous and criminal if you killed him in such a way. Calm yourself, I beg of you, for I will do your pleasure. You may consider me yours. I am yours and truly I do so desire. I told you nothing from pride but only in order to know you and to test you—to see if I could find out if you loved me with all your heart. However, I would in no way wish to see you commit treachery. Milord is not on his guard against you. If you were to kill him thus, you would be doing too great a treachery. And I would be held responsible. Everybody in the country would say that it had been done because of my worth.

"Go and rest until morning when my lord arises. At that time you can attack him without blame and without reproach." (Her heart thought what her mouth did not say.)

"Sir," she continued, "believe me. Don't be crestfallen, for tomorrow you can send in here your sergeants and your knights to carry me off by force. My husband, who is proud and courageous, will want to defend me. Then have him seized, or wounded, or his head cut off.

"I have led this life too long. I don't care for my husband's company. My lord, I am not trying to lie to you. I would already like to feel you naked against me in bed. Since we have come this far, you may be sure of my love."

"Till tomorrow then," the count answered. "You were certainly born at a good hour. You will be received most honorably."

149

"Sir, I believe it. First, however, I should like to have your word that you will love me dearly. I wouldn't believe you otherwise."

"Lady," the count answered happy and joyous, "I pledge you my troth. Loyally, like a count, I will ensure your life. Therefore don't worry about anything. You shall have everything your heart desires."

After the count had withdrawn, Erec and his wife went to their room where two small beds had been made, one for him and one for her. Since Erec had no inkling that he was in any danger, he fell asleep at once. Enide lay awake worrying until she saw the first streaks of light in the sky. She was afraid of waiting too long. Finally she awoke her husband. "Sire," she said, "pity! Get up quickly from here, for you have been betrayed without motive or provocation. The count is a proven traitor who, if he can find you, will not let you escape from this place. Don't wait any longer. The count wants me and therefore hates you. But if God pleases, who sees all things, you will be neither dead nor seized." Erec saw how loyally she loved him.

"Lady," he said, "have our horses saddled at once. Run call our host. Tell him to come here." Erec dressed and armed himself. Then he settled with his host by making him the very generous present of seven horses. After having warned his wife not to speak, Erec set forth. No sooner had they left the burgher's house than one hundred heavily armed knights appeared to capture Erec.

The count soon realized that he had been tricked. He and his men followed the fresh hoof tracks into the forest. "Whoever can give me the head of that knight," promised the count, "will be richly rewarded." His knights were drunk with anger against him whom they had never seen, against a man who had done them no injury. They caught sight of Erec just as he was riding into a covert of trees.

Enide heard the commotion behind her and the noise of

their arms and the hoofbeats of their horses. Turning around in the saddle, she saw that the valley was full of pursuers. She could not keep from speaking. "Oh, Sire," she cried. "Oh-h-h! This count is coming after you. Look at the host he is bringing with him. Sire, ride faster so we can get under the trees. Maybe we can escape that way, for they are still far behind us. If you keep going at this pace, you won't escape death. They are too many."

"You have a low opinion of me," Erec replied. "You consider my orders worthless. I don't know how to request you to do something well enough to correct your immoderate nature. But if God shows me mercy today in that He allows me to escape, you will be punished for this."

Erec turned in the saddle and saw the count's seneschal mounted on a fast horse, bearing down upon him. Despite the man's excellent armor, Erec pierced him with his pike. Then the count himself, who as the story says was a strong and accomplished warrior, spurred towards Erec. The foolish fellow had such over-confidence in himself, however, that he had taken that morning only a shield and a lance. At the impact his lance pierced Erec's shield but passed beside his body. Erec, on the other hand, pierced the count's shield and drove his blade into his foe's abdomen. As the count fell to the ground, Erec wheeled and dashed into the forest.

The hundred knights stopped beside their lord, whom they assured that they would ride for two or three days if necessary in order to capture or to kill Erec. "Sirs," the count told them feebly, "I say to you all that not one among you is daring enough to take another step forward in his pursuit. This goes for you all, strong and weak, high and low. Return home immediately, all of you. I have acted in a villainous fashion and I am sorry for it. The lady who tricked me is noble, honorable, and well-bred. It was her beauty alone that set me on fire so that I desired her. Therefore I wanted to kill her husband and hold her by force. Only evil could have been the outcome, and so misfortune has fallen upon me. What a felon I was! How treacherous and disloyal and evil I was! There was never a better knight of woman born than this one! He shall never receive any more trouble from me nor any trouble at all if I can help it. Therefore I order you home."

The party returned to their castle, bearing on his shield the body of the seneschal. The count was not wounded to death. He lived and Erec was saved once more.

After many other adventures Erec was so covered with wounds that one day he toppled from his saddle. He could proceed no further. Enide saw him fall. She ran towards him like a woman who cannot conceal her grief. She shrieked aloud and twisted her hands. She tore her clothes and her hair and her face. "Oh God," she cried. "Oh, my dear Lord, why do you leave me alive? If you are dead, then deliver me also." Then she fell fainting over his body. When she had recovered consciousness, she began to blame herself. "Oh, sad Enide, you have killed your husband! You have murdered him with words! He would still be alive if I had not spoken to him, outrageous and foolish woman that I was! It never hurts a man when a woman is silent in front of him; words often injure him. I have had experience and I know." Enide sat on the ground and held Erec's head in her lap.

"Oh, how wrong I was to speak such words to the most excellent of knights! In you Beauty saw herself mirrored. Your prowess was tried. Wisdom had given you her heart. Largess had her crown in you, without which there is no chivalry. . . . What did I do? I misunderstood you and I persisted. My outspoken words have caused your death. I am to blame—I alone.

"Oh, God, what shall I do? Why do I live so long? Why does Death stay and wait so long? Why doesn't Death take me now without delay? Death must consider me unworthy, since he is so disdainful of me. I must myself take revenge for my crimes. Thus I will die since Death won't assist me. I can't die from wishing for Death. Complaining is of no use. This sword which my husband wore will have to take revenge. Then I will never be in danger again, nor full of entreaties, nor wishful."

Enide drew the sword from the scabbard and sat looking at it. God, who is full of pity, held back her hand a little. Her cries had reached a count of high birth who was riding through the forest. (God did not wish Enide to be lost and forgotten.) She would have killed herself, too, if the count had not surprised her and taken the sword from her hand and thrust it back in the sheath. Then the count dismounted and inquired of her who the knight was and whether she was his sweetheart or his wife.

"One and the other, Sir," she said. "I am so grieved I can not tell you how much. I am sorry not to be dead also."

The count comforted her. "Lady, I beg you in God's name to have mercy on yourself. You have every reason to grieve, but you should not be totally desolate like this. You will be happy one day again. Don't lose all hope. Take comfort. God will give you other joys. . . . Your beauty, which is so fine, destines you for further adventures. I will take you as my wife. I will make you a countess and a fine lady. This should console you greatly. And I will have his body carried and interred with highest honors. Leave off this sorrow which you display so foolishly."

She answered, "Sir, go away! For the love of God, leave me be! You can't win anything here. Nothing you could say or do would ever draw me towards happiness."

The count stepped away and said, "Make a bier upon which we can carry the body. Then with the lady we will return at once to the castle of Limors and there bury the knight. Then I will marry the lady, for I never saw one so beautiful nor one I so much desired. I am very glad to have found her. Therefore don't spare any pains but make the bier quickly and as befits a knight." His men cut two poles across which they tied branches. Then they laid Erec on this litter and caught his horses. Enide rode beside the count who put his arm about her and held her up every time she fainted from grief.

They laid Erec in the great hall of Limors castle, the count's palace, where everyone—ladies, knights, and burgesses—came to see him. They set his lance and his shield beside him. The crowd filled the hall to overflowing. Everybody was curious to know the knight's name and story.

The count, meanwhile, consulted his barons privately. "Sirs," he said, "at once I want to receive this lady. We can perceive for ourselves that she is lovely and intelligent, that she is also of high lineage. Her beauty and her open manner show clearly enough that one could not do her greater reverence than to bestow a realm or an empire upon her. I shall never be the worse because of her, and I shall probably even be raising myself. Have my chaplain summoned and go seek the lady. I desire to settle upon her as a dowry the half of my lands—so she does my will."

Then the chaplain was brought and so was Enide, by force, for she absolutely refused to come otherwise. However, the count married her just as he pleased. As soon as the wedding ceremony was done, he ordered his constables to have tables set in the palace. The supper was soon ready, for it was past time.

It was after vespers, on a May evening, but Enide was frantic with sorrow. Her grief had not lessened. Beside her the count urged her by entreaties and by threats to smile a little and to take comfort. He had seated her in a great chair, whether she wished it or not. Then dinner was set before her. The count sat beside her. When he understood that he could not make her cheerful, he became quickly enraged.

"Lady," he said, "you must stop this sorrowing and you must forget. You can trust me to give you honors and wealth. You ought to know well enough that a dead man doesn't come back to life just because someone weeps for him. Nobody ever saw such a thing occur. Just remember from what poverty you came and into what riches! You were poor. Now you are rich. Fortune has not been niggardly towards you, when such honors are done and now that you can call yourself countess. It is true that your lord is dead; naturally you are sorry and upset. Do you think this amazes me? No! But I want to give you some advice, the best I know how to give: when I married you, then I gave you a reason for joy. So take care not to make me angry! Now, eat! And I so command."

"Sir," she answered, "I don't want to. Know for certain that as long as I live I shall never eat or drink again unless I see my lord who lies on that dais eat again."

"Lady, that cannot happen. People will consider you out of your mind when they hear you utter such follies. You would be very unreasonable to cause me to lose my temper."

By not even answering him, Enide showed that she cared nothing for his threats. For this, the count slapped her across the face. She cried out, and the barons who were in attendance reprimanded their count. "Stop, Sire," they told him. "You should be ashamed to strike a lady just because she won't eat. You have committed a bad action there. If this lady mourns for her husband whom she sees dead in front of her, we cannot blame her for that."

"Shut up, all of you!" cried the count. "The lady is mine, and I am hers. So I will do whatever I please with her." Then Enide could keep silent no longer. She swore that she would never be his. Then the count raised up in his chair and struck her again.

This time Enide screamed loudly. "Oh, you felon! I don't care at all what you say or what you do! I'm not afraid of your blows or your threats! I beat myself enough and strike my own self, too. You'll never hit me so hard that I will do anything more or less for you! Go ahead! Even pull out my eyes with your fingers or flay me alive."

From the midst of all these shouts and screams, Erec began to regain consciousness . . . just like a man awakening from a sleep. He opened his eyes and wondered who all these people around him were. Then he felt a stab of anguish when, through the commotion, he recognized his wife's hysterical voice. He got up from the dais sword in hand. His anger gave him strength—that and the love he bore his wife. He ran in her direction so fast that in a second he had struck the count across the head, brained him, and left him speechless and struck. His blood and brains flew out over the table.

The barons jumped up from their seats. They thought they were seeing the devil who had come inside the hall after them. Nobody stayed to see any more. Old and young were alike terrified. They fled one over the other as best they could, as fast as their legs could stride. Strong and feeble, all of them screamed: "Run! Run! See the dead man!" They knocked each other and jammed the exit. The bigger ones pushed and kicked the others in their haste to get out of there. Those who were last in the stampede tried to be the first out. Thus everybody bolted from the hall. Nobody waited for anyone else.

Erec ran for his shield which he fastened about his neck. Enide took his lance. Then they ran towards the open courtyard. Nobody was so bold as to approach them. Everybody thought that they were no longer ordinary folks but that devils or demons had suddenly entered them where they held sway over their bodies. Even as they fled, Erec pursued them close on their heels. Just as he came into the courtyard, he saw a groom leading his own war horse to water. The steed was still saddled and bridled. That was a fortunate chance. As Erec approached, the stable boy was frightened. He let go the horse.

Erec jumped into the saddle and leaned down for Enide. He lifted her up before him. The big horse bore them both easily. They found the door open. They galloped through it. There was nobody to stop them. . . . Those inside the castle had enough trouble with the count's lying dead at the table. There wasn't a single horseman of any estate who cared to ride in pursuit. . . . The count lay dead at the table. And Erec, who kidnaped his own wife, embraced her and kissed her, and comforted her.

Inside his arms and against his heart he held her close and said, "Sweet sister, I have tested you long enough. Do not be sad any longer. For I love you more now than I ever before did. And I am certain all over again and sure now that you love me perfectly. From this day forward I shall live according to your commandments. From this day hence I desire to be with you again as I was before. If you distrusted me in any way, I now pardon you and call it quits both for your distrust and for your words."

Then he kissed her and hugged her over and over again. Enide was not at all unhappy when her lord hugged her and kissed her and assured her of his love. They rode away through the forest. They traveled fast.

And it was a great sweetness to them that their way that night was lighted by the clear light of the moon.

VIII

THE ROMANCE OF THE CHÂTELAIN OF COUCY

Anonymous

THIRTEENTH CENTURY

OW I will leave the Châtelain of Coucy and will tell you that the Lady of Fayel was filled with joy as she never was before in her life. She wandered over to her bed and fell asleep with sweet thoughts. She slept until her husband, the Lord of Fayel returned, when she was obliged to dress for dinner. She wisely maintained her dignity and hid her feelings so carefully that no one could have guessed that she had bestowed her heart elsewhere than on her husband—so attentively did she serve him. On the other hand, the Châtelain ostensibly thought early and late only of tournaments—not of any love. He could not stay very long in any one place. As soon as he learned of a tournament, or a festivity, or a round table,

then he had to go there for adventure's sake. He performed so valiantly that his name lived. He was well known everywhere. And every time he returned secretly to his home, then he received a letter from his beautiful lady—so highborn and so charming. As soon as their messenger had made the arrangement, then the two met as I have already explained. This went on for a very long time without anyone ever being the wiser. Thus happily he lived his life with his sweet, pretty lady whom he often held close in his arms in joy and ecstasy.

Then it happened that one summer there was in Vermandois a very large festival of the gentry from far and near. There were ladies and knights, maidens and squires. The weather was lovely and clear—it was peace time—and people made merry to celebrate, to eat, drink, and be carefree. They only wanted to frolic, I think, without jousts or tournaments. Such sports are pleasant—and not perilous. The ladies were very gay; the knights bachelor most attentive.

The Châtelain was present, although he rather wished not to be there because his lady had come. The halls where the dinner was served were richly and tastefully adorned. Many noble people were present, all dressed in their finery. The ladies sat down to dinner beside the knights. It so happened that a lady from Vermandois whose heart was full to bursting with love for the Châtelain sat beside him at table. This lady was pretty and charming. She was also intelligent and malicious. For a very long time she had thirsted over the Châtelain, wondering how she could win his love. This reason caused her to sit beside him. She hoped by observing him closely to see if she could discover if he had a secret love. She had never heard in her life any story to that effect involving either lady or maiden. Often times she wondered sadly, "Where does his cheerful face come from, since he is not the lover of any lady? I think

160

he is in love and is beloved, but that he is prudent enough and careful enough to escape detection." She sat there thinking this and re-thinking it. She ate very little. . . . People were seated without order, here and there where they had happened to find a place. His dear lady, however, was at a table rather far away, next to a, famous knight. Once, when the Châtelain dared look in her direction, he met her eyes. That one time he could not help it. Her eyes in his caused him to heave such a sigh that the lady beside him asked what the matter was. He told her that he had felt a stab of pain, that it often caught him like that—it was an old malady. . . .

"Certainly, Sir," she told him. "I don't believe a word of it."

"Well," he replied, "what do you think is wrong with me?"

They did not speak further, for the lady began to sing a love song for the company. While everyone joined in the refrain, the servants continued to pass delicious dishes of which I shall speak only briefly. Then the Lady of Fayel took hand with the knights and ladies at her table and singing "I love him loyally" she led her party in a dance.

This party lasted for three days—dancing, caroling, and feasting. Jugglers came from all over the country, and they were well rewarded with clothing and gifts. Music was made for them with horns and bells and drums. There were games with monkeys and bears. Everyone made merry. Many a lover spoke to his beloved. But the Châtelain never once smiled nor exchanged a look with his lady except that one look and sigh the first evening. After the company had returned home again, he continued his apparently gay life of jousts and tournaments so carefully that by his deportment and his appearance no one could have had a suspicion that he ever gave so much as a thought to lady or damsel.

A painful spark of love, however, had caught in the heart

162

of the lady who had sat beside him at dinner. It burned her. She could not imagine that such a thing could be, that such a handsome bachelor, so full of chivalry, could live without a love. "He has a lover. I know it, for sure. I have failed with him. I would surely lose my pains if I gave my heart up to him. Yet I still don't know the truth, or the lady he loves. I suspect only one, and her because of what I saw the other yesterday. . . . They exchanged looks. His sigh gave me food for thought. . . . I shall never rest easy until I know for certain whether they are pledged to each other."

After much torment this lady decided to hire a spy to watch the Châtelain every time he went home in order to learn if he ever went privately to see the Lady of Fayel. The valet who undertook the assignment agreed to follow the Châtelain here and there, wherever he might go—both morning and evening, early and late. "I will give you so much money," she said, "that it will suffice."

The valet, dressed as a peasant, watched assiduously evening and morning before the door of the Châtelain's manor. Whenever he went out on errands here and there, the fellow followed him not far behind—one time far away and the next time near. He changed clothing often. The valet found lodging with a baker whose shop fronted on the sidewalk. One day he saw the maid carry a letter.

The Châtelain broke the seal and read eagerly. He was so happy to learn that he was expected that night at the little side door! He ordered his supper, washed and dressed, and sat down merrily to wait for darkness. When night came, he left his house as quietly as he could, only telling his valet not to expect him until daybreak. Then he set out . . . as if aimlessly. . . . He passed close to the clever spy who was hidden under some stairs. The Châtelain had no suspicion that he was being followed through the town, along the hedgerows and shrubs, up to the hidden door where he found the stone which meant the coast was clear. . . . The Châtelain waited hardly at all. The door was opened at once and at once closed after him. He went up to his lady's bedroom. They met with great joy. What is the use of my telling you? In each other's arms they pledged their love and took their delight.

As soon as the spy saw the Châtelain admitted through the little door, he returned to the village. By daybreak he was already racing home to announce his discovery. As soon as she saw him, she cried, "Tell me. Go on. Say what you found."

"Lady," he replied, "I will tell you and no lies." He told her truthfully how he had seen the Châtelain enter but that he had not waited to see him come out again.

"Oh," said the lady, "I know enough. It is certainly true just as I thought. Go now, and not a word of this."

The lady brooded over her jealousy for a month. She was so angry that her spoiling heart was like to have tainted her stomach. Then one day the Lord of Fayel stopped at her manor house for dinner. During the meal the lady ate so little that he noticed it. "What are you thinking about?" he asked her.

"Ha!" she replied. "I wish you did know what is annoying me, but I don't wish to arouse your wrath. You won't learn it from me today. You can learn it from others, for which reason I shall ask you to speak of this no more."

"Lady, I shall not speak of it until time and place are more suitable," he replied in a whisper. He decided to get it from her before he ever left her house; and, indeed, he later found an opportunity for being alone with her. He pleaded so well that she pretended not to be able to resist any longer.

"It weighs heavily upon me—so grievous is this news," she began. "The truth is that the Châtelain of Coucy and the lady of your house are in love and have been in love for a long time and do their will with no one to hinder them."

He said, "I can't believe that such words are true—nor that my wife does such a thing to me."

"I will tell you how to be sure of it," continued the lady. She then told him all about the secret door through which the Châtelain entered and how the Lord of Fayel could surprise the lovers.

In accordance with her instructions he returned home, where he put a good face upon his secret unrest. He told his own lady one Thursday morning that he had to be away for eight or so days. He left right after breakfast, taking only one trusted servant with him. Once they were out on the road, he confided in this squire, telling him that he had even checked on the little side door which he had thought sealed from long disuse. He had, indeed, found that it could be opened.

The squire took little stock of the whole story. He considered it an indication of slander and jealousy. However, as he and his master discussed the various possibilities, they decided to hide in a neighboring manor during the daytime so that every night they could watch in the park of Fayel. The valet particularly advised prudence, considering his mistress's blameless reputation, the Châtelain's valor, and the powerful families of the two. They watched in the park, the servant at the entrance to the woods and the master beside the vaulted door—on Friday night. They saw no one. They watched also on Saturday and again on Sunday. Still no one.

Then on Monday night they saw the Châtelain come through the trees and out across the park. He was dressed in full armor. He went directly to the door, stooped to look at a stone, rapped ever so lightly, and was admitted at once. The master waited a few more minutes to see whether or not the Châtelain came back out. He did not.

165

"Alas!" said the Lord of Fayel. "How tricked I have been and how wretchedly deceived!" He berated the squire, whose name was Gobert, for his having allowed the Châtelain to enter. This servant still did not believe his mistress to be implicated in any way. By pointing out the dangers of mistaken accusations, he persuaded his master to continue his watch until he had absolute proof. Therefore they resumed patrolling the grounds every night. Nothing happened for two more nights.

Then on a Thursday Gobert ran ahead to notify his master that the Châtelain was just coming through the woods. Without losing any time, the master stepped up to the door and knocked. Within a matter of seconds the door was opened by the lady-in-waiting. . . . It so happened that the mistress was ill that night and had already gone to bed. . . . Her maid therefore had been waiting inside the door, had opened it at once, had let in the person she thought was the Châtelain, and had immediately bolted the door. . . . The Châtelain's knock came almost at once. As soon as the master heard it, he slid back the bolt and opened the door himself. The Châtelain entered. It was so dark there in the passage that he did not see the Lord of Fayel. The lady-in-waiting was terrified.

It was she, however, who first took action. "Lord God!" she cried. "Who are these people?"

"I can inform you," snapped her master. "I know what you have been hatching so long around here. And I found it out. Châtelain, your disloyalty can be covered no longer. You will take orders from me now."

The Lady of Fayel heard all this from her bedroom where, shaking with fear, she huddled under the covers. She decided not to budge, as if she knew nothing of what was happening. She heard her master stamp about here and there and shout in a nasty voice for his household to assemble and bring some lights.

In perfectly regulated tones, the Châtelain drawled, "Sir, you could cause a great defamation of character by the way you are acting here. You should first hear what I have to say about this matter before you cast any aspersions upon a lady who is in no way guilty of any misconduct."

"Châtelain, I know whom to blame. I know for certain that you have not come and gone for anyone except for my wife."

"Oh, Sir," protested the Châtelain, "you say such willful words out of present wrath only. But I am here to swear that never in any day of my life have I addressed either words of flirtation or of love to your wife. I will say, however, that I have held her lady-in-waiting dear to my heart. You saw for yourself how she came here alone, without any other companion. Believe me, I pray you, when I say I know nothing of your wife. Gentle Sir, do not believe things about her which are untrue. . . . Such belief is a great sin."

From her chamber the lady heard what the Châtelain was saying. She got out of bed quietly and like a person versed in intrigue closed and bolted the door from her bedroom to her dressing room.

As the master listened to the Châtelain speaking so frankly and so politely, he did not know what to think. It seemed, on the face of it, fairly clear that his wife was not involved. Even so, he asserted from bravado, "Your words have no weight with me. I know you love someone higher than a lady-in-waiting. But you speak fancy words."

At this point the master heard Gobert outside the door. He let him in. The household servants had assembled with tapers. The squire Gobert bowed to the Châtelain. "God help me, Sir," he told him. "I am sorry to see you here."

"Oh?" replied the Châtelain. "Why is that? . . . By God above, Gobert, I am not afraid of you or of your lord. It is only my right to defend myself if you wish to hear me. I have secretly loved this lady-in-waiting for some time

167

now. So I came to see her. I don't know who told your lord something else. He who dares say otherwise is mistaken. And especially those who accuse his wife. I stand ready and willing to take an oath on it or to make a formal denial, whichever he says. And not because I am afraid, you understand, but only because I wish him to correct his present error."

Then the lady-in-waiting stepped forward. "You speak the truth," she said to the Châtelain. Then she turned to her master. "He came and went because of me, and will again, if you please, either here or wherever I may be. I did no wrong in loving him. Therefore, Sir, do not be so upset nor so furious. If you want to dismiss me, I know where to go. My lady knows nothing of this. I concealed my actions so carefully that she has never suspected anything. I know she will learn about tonight and that she will probably discharge me tomorrow."

Having overheard all this, the Lady of Fayel began to scream upstairs. "Help! Help!" she cried. "What people are shouting down there? What do I hear? Are there robbers in the house?"

When Gobert saw that her door was locked, he showed it to his master. "Look, Sire," he said. "You see that your lady knew nothing. Admit that you were mistaken. She was in bed with her door locked. That's apparent."

They found the Lady of Fayel standing trembling beside the main door to her room. "Who's there?" she kept asking.

"Lady, your lord is here. He just now found Sir Ernaut de Coucy who had come in by a side door in the garden," Gobert told her.

"God," she said. "That can't be!"

"Yes, Lady, very truly true. Come quickly and help us set him free, for your lord wants to kill him." The lady hesitated no longer. She followed Gobert downstairs where the men were arguing fiercely.

168

When her lord saw her, he said, "Lady, it was my right to spy upon you in order to see what evil doings were going on around here. The Châtelain who came so often spent Monday night here, and I know it. I shall take my vengeance upon him and also upon you if I can."

Bursting into tears, she said, "Sire, do not believe that I ever committed any folly as far as you are concerned. I would rather die than act in such a way. I never spoke words of love to the Châtelain, and no man ever loved me since I married you. May God be my witness. And also, it is not very chivalrous of him to have brought blame and shame upon us. For those who hear about this will think he came for me. I am very disobliged to him and even more so to Isabelle who could lead such a life, for her way of living is bad and ugly. So help me God, I knew nothing about it. I could not have named any gentlewoman in the country less disposed to prayers and pledges of love than her!"

"Well, truly," said the Lord of Fayel, "this is a wonder. I must be dried up above the ears. I don't know what to say or think, so well do you know how to bow me out. Now I don't know what to do. I am completely amazed at this business. Well! As much as I suffer, so much must I expedite it. Therefore, Châtelain, you will leave, taking Isabelle with you, for she shall never sleep under this roof again."

"Sire," said Gobert, "if he does, then that would be too great a scandal. You know that she is a gentlewoman and cousin to my lady. Wouldn't everyone know her situation if you ordered her out in such a way? She could go home quietly in eight days or so, saying she no longer wished to stay. Thus by your leave and your generosity, she could hold up her head."

"Let it be thus," answered the master. "Now, Châtelain, swear that you never attempted to dishonor me, nor to cast blame upon me, nor shame; that you never pursued

169

my wife for love, nor for your amusement, nor for your delight; and that you will never seek her in your life, and that you did not come here because of her."

"I so guarantee," said the Châtelain, "and I swear to all of it according to your request. But out of friendship I beseech you to believe that this lady knew nothing. For it would be too great a sin upon me—as I hope my own soul will be saved—to have implicated her in any way."

"I still don't know how I shall settle this all the way through," replied the Lord of Fayel, "for the more I think about it, the less good I find in it. So, go now without delay."

Gobert unlocked the door as quickly as he could. The Châtelain left without uttering another word. He was so afflicted that he did not even say goodnight. Gobert walked home with him. Along the road the Châtelain pressed him so with questions that he finally revealed how his master had been warned, and he named the lady of Vermandois by name. This pleased the Châtelain very much.

"Now go back, Gobert, and tell your master for me that I hereby give him fair warning. On my word, if I ever learn that out of spite he strikes his lady or causes her any discomfort whatsoever, he will find me not only his bitter enemy but I will wage such a war against him that there won't be anywhere in all his lands a stronghold where I will not bring him to his humiliation and degradation. And for the spite he vented on me, I am annoyed and made ugly. Tell him that I accept this insult for the sake of his wife's honor. If he wishes to let it go at this, I will say he is a shrewd man. If, on the other hand, he wants to bring it to blows with me, both his body and his vassals will come to their grief."

"Sire," Gobert argued, "know that great mischief comes from wars. If I can, I will settle this matter quietly. Please don't hold it against me because I was with him tonight. I only did it with the best of intentions. Also, dear Sir, you will find me eager to do your will."

"Sir," replied the Châtelain, "my very great thanks."

When Gobert arrived back at Fayel, he found the master holding forth in a storm of anger. He was giving his wife and his household a riotous night.

"Please, Sire," said Gobert. "Be silent. Calm yourself. You are rioting here for nothing. I hope you will go right to bed; for too long and without reason are you causing such strife." Gobert said so much, this way and that way, that the master stopped quarreling; but he did not come out of his jealousy and will not come out of it as long as he lives. No one could make him believe that the Châtelain had not come inside for his wife. However, he began to consider how he could work it in order to find out for sure. He decided to stop talking about it—as if nothing had happened. Once he made up his mind what to do, he went to bed with his wife.

The master's heart was full of wrath, for Gobert had given him the Châtelain's message about the war he would wage. He ate his heart out thinking that if he ever got the Châtelain in his power again he would never a second time let him out alive. However, he gave no more signs of wanting to trap him. He secretly repented of ever having let him go. Three days later he ordered his wife to dismiss Isabelle. Then he ransacked his castle up and down, blocked up the path through the park, and walled up the little door.

On her side the lady tried to think how to disinvolve herself. She was furious at having been spied upon. She knew how jealous and envious her husband was. In order to give him the lie, she scolded Isabelle in his presence. "I certainly never thought that such a thing would happen to me through you and your actions," she told her. As long as her husband was within earshot, the lady continued to reproach Isabelle. He was therefore more confused than ever.

171

As soon as he had left the room, however, then you would have seen both their faces streaming with tears! They mourned for the early days which would never come back again. They were sad for all the pleasant times they had so enjoyed. The love, which they had thought the best hidden in the world, had fallen upon evil days. Then the lady thanked Isabelle for the shame and dishonor she had taken upon herself.

"Lady," said Isabelle, "there isn't a thing I could do to please you that I would not do willingly. Do not worry if I see my own way clearly. You will see the Châtelain often. Let's see how he can come to speak to you. Just remember to take great thought so that Milord does not surprise you. He won't fail to stretch cords to trip you. If you could manage to tie Gobert to your bow, that would be a fine stroke." Then Isabelle said farewell to all—to both small and great—for she was very much loved in the household.

The Châtelain meanwhile had never been so angry in his life. He took especial pains to hide it, however, and confided in no one. He would never be easy, he thought, until he took revenge upon the lady who, from envy, had ruined the sweet life which he had led so long and so tranquilly. He lay in bed thinking until noon every day, without having closed his eyes in sleep. He thought of one idea after another, got up and dressed, had dinner, and then wandered about not caring where he went. Every place bored him. His heart was heavy from morning to night—heavy and sad, sorrowful and pensive. He only hoped that Love, through its lofty sway, would tell him not to be dismayed, and that he would again take delight with his sweetheart. Meanwhile, he wrote many new love songs.

When the Châtelain had decided upon a course of action, he called for his armor, his horses, and his harnesses. He set out for a tournament so that night would fall as he passed the manor of Vermandois. He sent his servant ahead to ask for hospitality. The lady of Vermandois was in the courtyard. Her husband, a courteous and gallant knight, had accompanied some friends to a tournament. When she learned that the Châtelain sought shelter for the night, she was not at all displeased. She immediately invited him to be her guest, ordered her cooks to prepare a fine dinner, and welcomed the Châtelain in person.

"I am thankful it is so late," she told him with a laugh, "for if it had been daylight, you would never have stopped. You have often passed by this way without making much ado about us."

"Lady," the Châtelain told her abruptly, "you may be sure that when I left home I fully intended to come here."

Chatting easily, the lady led her guest into a small field where the table was set for supper. It was very pretty and delightful there on the bright grass. The Châtelain's thoughts were all of his Lady of Fayel. His hostess had gone to a great deal of trouble with her meal and its serving. When she saw him so silent, she hesitated. Then she said, "God willing, you will admit to me how pensive you are. It must be love that makes you so thoughtful."

"You are certainly right, Lady," he replied. "Love binds me to his service night and day. I wish you knew my suffering and felt it also."

"Good Sir," laughed the lady, "it would hardly be proper for me either to know it or to feel it. I would only be beating the bushes for another lady's game." They finished their supper in a leisurely manner and went to sit on the pretty lawn. The servants had gone about their business.

The Châtelain was eager to begin his speech, for he was anxious to have done with it. "When I listen to you, Lady, I imagine, according to what you say, that you have me all established as the lover of some lady or some maiden. But I will swear to you on my soul, milady, that you yourself are the one I have loved for so long. I am yours utterly."

173

"Come, Châtelain, how can you think you have hid your true love that I don't know who she is? We all know it— and so does the little door."

The Châtelain grew pale. He did not reply until he was in perfect control, however. "Milady, you will say what you so desire or shall desire, but never once in my life did I ever have a love or a flirtation worthy of report. I may, in order to amuse myself, have had an affair with a chambermaid who was not so dear to me that I care to celebrate her. I consider you so cultured that you would hardly wish me not to aim higher. Aside from yourself, I never cared to pledge my heart."

Then the Châtelain went on his knees, begging her to grant him some jewel or token that he could wear as a sign of her favor. He would defend it in the next tournament. The lady believed that there would be no harm to herself in this since all he could do would be to lose the favor of any other lady he might love.

"Ask what you will, Sir Knight," she replied. "I have a beautiful scarf woven with gold threads and a band set with jewels. I should like your promise beforehand that you will wear it without fail and that you will not exchange if for another."

"Milady, I am breathless with joy at your great favor. I shall never wear another than this one your pleasure is to give me. I must derive from it the will power to do you great honor in the jousts."

I haven't retained all their words nor can I speak at any length about their closeness except to say that before the Châtelain left, he had received from her a promise of all he sought. His heart was light because he saw how he could exploit her as much as he thirsted to do—her who had slandered the lady for whom he languished night and day. . . . He and the lady spoke no more that night. Each retired to his bed chamber. As soon as it was daylight, the

Châtelain—who had not been able to sleep—rose and set out for the jousts.

In Fayel the lady was in a state of very great anger because she had been deprived of Isabelle. No pleasure could distract her. She wondered whether or not she dared confide in Gobert. Finally she decided that she should because by remaining silent she would lose everything anyway. She planned to turn him to her side by sounding him out and by confiding in him if she found him at all disposed to aid her. It is no wonder she did this. Love, which caused the turmoil in her heart, was prompting her conduct. . . . She found him in the garden one day. In order to test him, she inquired how he had come to spy upon her.

"Sweet Lady," Gobert answered, "of all the knights in this land the Châtelain is the most respected and loved. No one can compare to him. No one is more chivalrous nor more accomplished. I love him dearly myself, and I would willingly do his pleasure to ensure his honor. I have taken his money. If I let Isabelle be sent away, I did it for your sake. And I also know for a fact that the Châtelain has loved you for years. He can't hide that from me. I know it for a fact. Rather than let any harm come to the bachelor, I would allow my own limbs to be cut off. That was clear, wasn't it? The other night, if I had wanted to bring him to grief, I think an evil thing would have occurred, for the master certainly intended to kill him. It would have been a sin and a pity for such an accomplished knight to have died by such a mischance. And if God grants me the occasion, I will speak to him soon and tell him that I can perhaps help you both. I think he would be willing to put me to trial."

"I think you are trying to trap me," said the Lady of Fayel, "so stop such talk. I don't care to hear it. But I assure you that I never even thought of any man except my husband. He is everything that should please me. Therefore let us say no more about the Châtelain, for I could never

175

love him. Nor would I set my heart on him. That would be open folly. One cannot lead love as one would like to do. Oh, I don't say that the Châtelain is not knightly and of great valor. However, a lady who wishes to do something contrary to her lord will fall into worse days, and that's my opinion."

"Lady," said Gobert, "how shall I speak of such things when I really know nothing at all? The only thing is that I often thought the Châtelain never came here and never committed such folly just for the sake of Isabelle. I feel sure of it. But that's neither here nor there. You do not wish to reveal anything to me, and I must accept that. But I know how the master came to accuse you, but I won't tell you since you do not wish to learn anything."

"Oh, yes, gentle Gobert, do tell me, I pray you."

Thus the Lady of Fayel learned how they had been denounced and by whom. "If you were to betray me, Gobert," she told him, "you would gain little by it."

"You may be sure that I wouldn't dare," he assured her, "for I know that the Châtelain in such an event would instantly kill me with his own hands."

Gobert then suggested that the lady pretend to dislike him and that she abuse him so often before her husband that Gobert would have an excuse for leaving the household. He also warned her that her husband would never be rid of his jealousy, but that he would guard her more and more closely. Since he had stopped attending tournaments, Gobert would have an added reason for asking to change households. "I will tell the master," Gobert added, "that I would like to join the Châtelain of Coucy, if I had permission to do so. As he knows, the Châtelain is the most valiant and skillful knight in the country. He will consent to this because he will thus hope to learn what transpires between you and the Châtelain. He will think I don't dare conceal anything from him."

"You have offered to do a great service, Gobert," said the lady, "and you have comforted me greatly."

"Don't be disheartened. I'll put all my wits to it." Then the lady gave him a large purse full of gold and a token by which the Châtelain would know he came from her. They spoke no more, for just then the Lord of Coucy returned from inspecting his wheat and his fields. Eight days later Gobert left the Lord of Coucy's service. He found the Châtelain at a tournament where he won all the prizes and wore the scarf of the lady of Vermandois. He was very glad to learn that the Lady of Fayel was safe and well and also to have Gobert in his service.

After the tournament the Châtelain rode away at once to the lady of Vermandois. She was at home alone and expecting him. Without further ado she granted him a private meeting in a lonely field where only heather grew—and this for the following Monday evening.

As far as the Lady of Fayel was concerned, there was neither joy nor any more gladness. Her husband stayed close to the manor house, both early and late. Nothing could make him leave it. He was full of anger, bad temper, wrath, and jealousy despite the fact that he had no new occasion for suspicion. His wife served him and did him honor. She tried very hard to beguile him from his brooding thoughts. A passing herald added to their misery by praising the Châtelain's gallant deeds and by saying that he wore a lady's favor on his helmet.

Before Monday night the Châtelain had instructed Gobert and Isabelle in what he wanted them to do. Then he awaited the lady in the deserted spot. "Lady, it's perfect to be with one's lover in such a pretty spot. The grass is fresh with dew and sprinkled with flowers. Let us sit here and lead a lover's life."

The lady replied, "That is the reason why I came. Love led me here to do your will. No one can resist Love, no matter how he tries to escape. I would struggle in vain against Love if I knew nothing about it."

Thus they talked for a long time, but—to make a true story short—he put her in such a plight that he could have accomplished his will without contradiction and without danger if he had wanted to choose the kind of pleasure a lover takes with his lady love. Suddenly, however, the Châtelain rose to his feet in great anger. "Look here, Lady," he said. "It's not your fault that your husband is not deceived. You have as much honor towards him as a whore, and for that I now shame you for having slandered someone better than yourself. May you burn in fire before I become your lover! . . ." At these words, and more, Gobert and Isabelle strolled by to witness the lady's predicament. For all she knew, there were other persons present in the woods.

"Alas! I am dead and betrayed!" she said. "I shall never regain my honor nor recover from my shame. So many people have seen me that it will be known everywhere soon! . . . False Châtelain, you have acted like a disloyal traitor who pretends to be loyal!"

"Lady, your own evil thoughts and your deeds and your words spoken like a fool's brought you to this. You will be forever blamed." The lady went home and buried her chagrin carefully.

After this adventure Gobert returned to Fayel where he finally was able, after much difficulty, to speak privately to the lady. He delighted her with his story of how she had been avenged, and together they began to plan how the lady and the Châtelain could meet again.

Both lovers therefore took heart, and the Châtelain composed a lovely song in celebration of spring. It was Gobert who arranged their next meeting. During the Lord of Coucy's absence he had the knight come to the castle all swathed in bandages, as if he had just been wounded. The Châtelain was put to bed in the castle. After dinner, when the household slept, then he crept to the lady's room. Their joy was impossible to express. They told each other what they had suffered, but all was forgotten since they could spend a night together. Just as dawn broke, the lady sent her lover away. The two parted with many last embraces— and in tears.

Soon after this parting the Lord of Coucy insisted upon taking his wife on a pilgrimage with him. The lady immediately sent word of this to the Châtelain, hoping that he could find some way to see her during this trip, for otherwise the castle was so well guarded that there was no further opportunity for him to come to her. The Châtelain sent word to her that he would be in a mill which she and her husband would pass.

When they arrived beside the mill, their valets let the horses wade out into the water to drink. The lady followed. As soon as her horse had bent down his head to the water, without saying a word the lady let herself fall into the stream. She suffered greatly from the cold, for there was ice and frost along the banks. Her servants pulled her out of the water, held her up by the arms, and helped her into the mill. There was no place for her to undress in the mill and no fire, but the miller said there was a bed and some blankets in a tiny room. He unlocked the door. The lady entered alone. Then the miller bolted the door after her. Her husband and the servants rode on into town to fetch some dry clothes and to care for the horses. . . . The lady was left alone with her lover.

"Lady," the Châtelain told her, "you have done so much for me that I do not know how to repay you. You have deserved a hundred times more than I could have deserved in a hundred years, nor repaid either, for all the cold you have endured."

"It was love," said the lady. "My pain is all gone when I hold you in my arms." They remained in the little room all morning . . . until the valets returned with clothing. They knocked at the door. The lady unbolted it to take the garments which they brought. Then she closed it and told them to wait for her until she was dressed. Then she mounted her palfrey and rode to a hotel in town.

The Châtelain remained in the mill until he could leave unseen. He paid the miller for his services.

After the pilgrimage the Lord of Coucy was even more hateful than before. He put all his ugly thoughts into words and abused his wife vilely. His anger, however, did not lose all control—not to the extent of actually killing his wife even though that was his desire. He realized by this time that Gobert was advising the Lady of Fayel and serving her rather than himself. Therefore the master pondered day in and day out over his revenge. It occurred to him that if the Châtelain were out of the country, then he would have no more worries. If he could manage to induce the Châtelain into taking the cross and going overseas—once he had pledged himself—he could not unsay it. He confided this plan to no one and concealed his thoughts in this matter. Once he had hit upon this solution he began to stop reviling his wife. For two months he acted as if he had forgotten his suspicions.

One time when he and his wife were lying together and playing at love games, he told her in beautiful words that he had always longed to go to the Holy Land. "Lady, I have had such a desire long past, and my heart has never changed. I should like to make this pilgrimage and this sainted voyage to the land that is across the sea. And also I should like to take you with me. In my company there will be many gallant knights and many ladies. We would both go of our own good will and for the forgiveness of our sins, for I should really like to have a pardon. So tell me your opinion of this project—of this voyage that is so worthily planned. Tell me you will come with me."

At first the lady was stunned, but not at such a loss for words that she did not keep her wits about her. After some reflection she saw through his words: he intended to put a good distance between her and the one she loved without guile.

Therefore she answered her master, "Oh, kind Sir, I thank God that you are showing me such great love and doing me such a great honor, for I could never wish more for anything than to go along the holy route. I will assist you with all my strength and do whatever I can to make this possible." While her tongue said one thing, her thoughts were elsewhere.

After the lord had got up out of bed, the lady began to think again about how she could handle this situation. She suddenly burst into tears, so upset was she over this new obstacle. She was incapable of a clear thought or a simple action. However, she presented a calm face to her lord whom she still hoped she was deceiving. She took comfort in one possibility. When the time to go arrived, she could pretend to fall ill so that they would have to leave her sick in bed. Her lord would be obliged to leave her and go for fear of being perjured or branded a coward. She thought and thought without succeeding in finding a way to tell this new development to the Châtelain.

One day she noticed a peddler. They were wandering tradesmen who traveled about the countryside with their wares of cloth and thread in a little basket hung about their necks. They had free access to manors and halls and houses in all seasons. No one paid much attention to them. This gave the lady an idea. She then managed to notify the Châtelain that she would be home alone on such and such a day when her husband had a lawsuit of some importance. Could the Châtelain come dressed as a merchant with a basket hung about his neck?

Gobert found the Châtelain at home. He therefore delivered the lady's letter without any delay. The Châtelain replied to the letter at once and as a double precaution instructed Gobert to tell his mistress that all would be as she desired. At Gobert's return the master was in the hall. As soon as he left, Gobert gave the lady the Châtelain's letter. She rushed into her dressing room to read it. It made her very happy.

The Lord of Fayel had a long conversation with his wife in which he reasoned with her. "Milady," he said, "now the time is drawing near when I am about to accomplish what I have vowed to do. I am delighted to have your consent to my suggestion that we both go overseas together. You will also win a pardon for yourself. Within a few more days I shall have finished putting my affairs in order, particularly in the matter of my cousin's lawsuit which will be adjourned Tuesday next. I will go into Vermandois, for it is only right to assist a member of my line."

"Sire," she answered, "you will be doing a great honor and favor in assisting your cousin, for she is a good and a quiet woman. It is only reasonable that you should appear in court to second her in her plea."

The Châtelain meanwhile had set about preparing his procedure. First he obtained a peddler's basket. Then he bought a pair of old shoes and a smock of gray wool with a wide hood, an old torn hat for his head, and a little iron-tipped stick to support the weight of the basket. Then he dyed his face with a brown stain and so changed his appearance that a person would have had to examine him most minutely ever to recognize him.

When he was satisfied that he was, to any casual observer at least, completely unrecognizable, the Châtelain set out eagerly along the road to Fayel. He watched through the trees for the first sight of its towers. By nine o'clock in the morning he was approaching the manor. When he saw its gray walls, he bowed low and said softly as if in prayer:

"Inside those ramparts stays the one who is a god to me. Jesus, grant that I may see her today and that I may hold her naked in my arms."

As he stood gazing towards Fayel, the Châtelain saw a party riding down the road towards him. On the lead horse he recognized the Lord of Fayel. They had already come so close that there was no hope of turning off the road to hide in the trees. Therefore the Châtelain bowed as low as he could and remained there beside the road. As he rode by the Châtelain, the Lord of Fayel waved at him and called, "Go straight ahead of you to my estate of Fayél. I hope you have some trinkets that milady and her attendants require."

The Châtelain remained humbly bent as if in respect until the party had passed. Then as fast as he could run—his head and arms bent over the bobbing basket—he hurried to the entrance of the manor. The gate was unbarred. The lady herself was sitting on the drawbridge waiting for him. She looked at the peddler and could hardly believe her eyes —that this must be he whom she longed so to see. She walked towards him smiling and teasing. "Where do you come from, handsome merchant? You have really come to me at the right time, for there is no one at home but me. My lord and his lady cousin whom he has had here to guard me night and day have gone to settle her property suit. I'm here all alone and unwatched. The servants are all at work in the courtyard. Let's go upstairs then—and be welcome."

She took him by the hand and led him up to her chamber where she had then all that her heart desired. There she could see the jewels he had brought her and chose the prettiest for herself. And the peddler without delay slipped the basket from his shoulder and enfolded her in his arms. He kissed her face—kisses that the lady returned gently. There in that room they were lovers once more—loving, sweet, pleasant, and delightful. . . . Then they sat side by side and talked of better days long past. There they re-made their hearts afresh and comforted one another and found peace again after their long suffering. The lady told him how her lord planned to go overseas and take her with him and how sad her heart was at that thought.

The Châtelain consoled her, as always. "Do not upset yourself about that," he said. "I tell you, if God permits it, that I will find a way to take the cross also so that I may see you often. My heart would be too full of anguish if I were not able at least to see you often."

Then they spoke about how they would manage to see each other again, and then about how he could manage to spend that night in the castle without arousing the servants' suspicions, and how he could steal up to her room where he had so often spent the night. They had made their plans so carefully that when the household assembled from their distant tasks which the lady had set for them, the peddler displayed his wares. The field workers had all returned because the rain fell so heavily that they could no longer work outside. They were glad to see the wares. First the lady handled them and bargained with the peddler. Then each one bought something for himself. The peddler haggled with them all and ended by exacting his price. He had no more tricks to learn about buying and selling, for he had studied it all beforehand until he had acquired a mastery of those techniques. When his wares were all gone, he closed his basket, rolled up his pack, and then said, "You have all kept me here too long in such bad weather. Look at the rain coming down! And listen to that wind! How shall I ever get home tonight to my hostel?"

"You cannot go out in that weather, friend," said a servant. "You will stay here tonight, with the lady's permission."

"Let him stay with no more ado," said the lady. "The poor merchant man and stranger!"

"Gentle Lady, may God bless you," said the peddler humbly. The lady smiled to see the proud Châtelain answer her so respectfully and with such humility. Then they chatted until supper was served. The hours dragged by too slowly for the Châtelain. Even though the lady requested him to have supper, he could not eat. He said that food would only aggravate his illness. Therefore the lady had a bed prepared for him. . . . He lay there pretending to be ill, unable to sleep, while his heart raced joyously at the thought that he would once more for hours and hours hold his sweet love in his arms. After the household had finally settled down for the night, he tiptoed across the great hall and up to the room where she lay awake waiting for him to come. There they lived in joy—lover and beloved.

There is one thing I know that is true. Love is the sovereign good that a person could wish for or have. I care nothing for gold or possessions, for castles or cities or other wealth. I care only for love. No other goods can attain its high estate. Nor does any man ever have greater joy. Never is a man handsomer, more joyous, more laughing and gay than when he is in love, especially when he lives in the hope of love's delights. Therefore all people should carefully treasure this rare gift of love and take all pains to deserve it by keeping the faith and by service.

This is what he of whom I speak had done, without ostentation and without foolishness of any kind, so that he deserved no unkindness at the hands of Love. This particular night he was rewarded beyond all his desires. It only saddened him to know that the hours would be too short. . . . As soon as he saw the first streaks of light in the sky, he returned to his room. He lay there wide awake until dawn. Then he rose, pulled on his smock and his garments, put on his hat and his hood, and tied his burden about his neck again. He took leave and went sadly away. Gobert awaited him with his own clothes in a designated spot. He was safely home in a few hours. On the way he told Gobert how the lady and her husband were leaving shortly for the Holy Land.

"According to my understanding, Sire," Gobert said, 'you should go on this pilgrimage also, for you can enjoy her more outside the country than here. I understand that King Richard has cried a tournament through England, and that it will be a marvelous event. Many knights from Vermandois will cross the sea to tourney with him. You could pass over with them and be in their company. Then there will be no trouble about your taking the cross along with them. He will have his Crusade* preached right after the tournament, I hear, and also he will take vows along with his knights. No one will guess your real motive for going overseas."

Within a few days the Châtelain traveled into England with a party of knights. It was the most magnificent tournament England ever had. Great knights, and all the greatest from distant lands, had journeyed there to uphold their lofty names. At the end of the first day's events King Richard inquired the names of the winners. Among them was the Châtelain of Coucy. The King invited the Châtelain to join his personal attendants and be a member of his most esteemed gentry. For eight days King Richard sat in plenary session of his court. A cardinal came to preach of Jesus who died on the cross to save their souls and redeem them from sin. Should we not also be mindful of Him? Should not our hearts catch on fire at the memory of His holy tomb across the sea? Should we not receive His cross in our hands and pledge our vows to Him?

Why make a long story of it? King Richard crossed himself and so did many a count, and after them many a knight rose from his knees and took the cross. King Richard was

* Medieval authors did not know this word.

pleased to see so many gallant knights from Vermandois make vows after him. The king was neither stingy nor mean. He handed out gifts to all—jewels of gold and silver as tokens of his love. He told them he would cast off around mid-August, regardless of cost, to pass over the sea and wage war on the pagans of the Holy Land. As soon as the king dismissed them, his newly sworn knights returned to their own domains to set their affairs in order. Their fame spread like wildfire through Vermandois.

A minstrel returned to Fayel with this news. The Lord of Fayel, who was very fond of minstrelsy and very generous with his wealth when he entertained them at his board, received him cordially. "Who won King Richard's tourney?" he asked. "Those of England or those of Ireland?" The minstrel told him the whole story. He lingered long over the high deeds and chivalry of their neighbor, the Châtelain of Coucy. When the Lord of Fayel learned that the Châtelain had already taken holy vows, he could not contain his joy. The lady also was joyous, for she had been desirous of this news. That day both husband and wife agreed. Both were happy. Their thoughts disagreed, however, since she wanted to go and he intended to stay. He still hid his thoughts as he had so carefully done up to that time.

The Châtelain had arrived home in Coucy, carefree and gay. He longed ardently for the day when both he and the lady would set out on this great journey. He had much work to do, many arrangements to make. He bought new horses and magnificent harnesses and weapons fit for a king, or a duke, or a prince, or a count. He took care to be beautifully outfitted on all occasions so as to maintain his reputation and inspire respect. His heart was so glad that he put his thoughts into song:

> When violet, May, and nightingale
> Summon my heart to sing,

187

Do not refuse me this one thing:
Dear God, hear my wish this spring:
To hold in my arms my naked love
Only once more before journeying.

The lady, on the other hand, was always about her lord,
insisting early and late that he cross himself and that he
hurry and that he finish his preparations. But milord
whiled away the days and let the time pass when he should
have been busy. He kept giving her faint promises that he
would do all his arrangements quickly and at the last moment. When all those who had taken vows were just about
ready to leave, it was Saint John's Day. Then one of the
cardinals came into the area to bless the new Crusaders.
The lady and her lord set out for the minster to hear him
preach. He began a great sermon about how many gentle
folks had taken the cross out of devotion and for the salvation of their souls. He called upon others to rise and approach the cross.

The lady rose to her feet, thinking to take the holy vows;
but her husband stopped her in time. He had known all
along that women would not be allowed to go overseas on
the Third Crusade. He therefore stood before her and
blocked her passage to the altar. "Lady," he said, "I won't
take the cross after all, this time. I feel I am too weak and
in too delicate health. This is why I do not dare undertake such an enterprise at this time. I cannot endure hardship, which is my real consideration. I have a weakness of
the heart which will keep me at home." They watched all
the others who had come for that purpose advance to the high
altar, make their vows on bended knees, receive the cross, and
return home to their manors and lodgings. Very quietly and
simply the lady covered her anguish and lowered her eyes.

As soon as she was alone at home, then she gave free
vent to her despair. Then she could scream and sob and

weep. "Oh, my beloved! Oh, my sweetheart! Now I see how you have been betrayed! And I also have been betrayed! Well may I now become desolate when I see that I must remain here while you will go over the sea. Oh! how far away from you I shall be! Alas! How shall I manage now to have news of you? Surely I shall die of grief. Never now shall I escape from death. Oh, what a cruel liar my husband was when he told me he would cross himself. He only did it to send you away from me. He used me to persuade you to take vows and to plan your voyage—and to do it for love of me. . . . He seemed so honest and frank with me, but all the time his own heart was veiled. He only pretended to be about to take a voyage, saying only to me those things which he did not mean at all. Alas! Why did I not understand the true sense of his treason and of his refusal? I myself was in a fever of desire to have my beloved leave this land. I myself labored to betray him!"

She went almost out of her mind with grief. She twisted her hands. She could not close her eyes in sleep. She did not know what to do. Her only consolation was in her memory. Finally her faith in the Châtelain restrained her and counseled her to calm her agitation and lessen her pain. Her own knowledge of him gave her a tiny ray of hope. It whispered a promise to her that he would come to her very soon—that she would not have long to wait. Thus the dictates of hope helped her to abstain from the depths of despair. Instead of lamenting, she tried to use her wits—tried to see how she could exploit even her adversity. Therefore she wrote the Châtelain, telling him how they had been duped into a crueler separation.

When the Châtelain read her letter, he thought his heart would burst. In his pain and distress he felt his heart severely tried and all his joy banished at once. He could find no consolation in her words. He felt such stabs of pain as he studied her letter that he could not contain himself. He

189

was plunged almost to utter despair. All his dear hopes—that the lady would pass overseas with him, where he would have at long last opportunities to see her and love her—were undone. He feared that he would never see her—perhaps never, never speak to her again. He mourned as he had never before mourned in all the world.

"Alas!" he sighed. "I see also how through envy I have fallen and been betrayed. How grief-stricken may I well be now that I must depart far from her who is all my desire. I know well enough that if I withdrew my oath and remained in this land, all would say without contradiction that I did it because of her. Then her husband would set such guards about her person that I should never again be able to speak to her. That way there is an utter loss.

"I see clearly enough that I must depart. Were I to stay, I would only bring both upon her and upon myself the ugliest of defamation...." The Châtelain confided in Gobert

"Do not lament like this," the squire told him. "Without fail, when we have acquitted ourselves and made such a long voyage and done great deeds in the name of God our Creator, then we will return home and be among the very first to be discharged. Think how hopeful you will be after all this. Think only about the joys of your return."

"On my word," the Châtelain replied, "your counsel is not bad. All we can do now is to find a way for me to speak to her privately. She writes me that her husband is convoked to a meeting of Parliament in Paris. She also asked me to send Isabelle to see her."

The Châtelain disguised himself as a blind beggar, with a torn surcoat and tattered robe. He walked along the road into Fayel, tapping the ground with his staff. The lady and Isabelle were seated on a stone beside the gate. They had been waiting for him. Isabelle led the blind man across the courtyard. They met no one. The house staff were all at work. As soon as Isabelle notified the lady that he was safely inside her room and that no one had seen him come, the lady ran as fast as she could go. The Châtelain had already thrown off his torn, brown robes. He stood before her resplendent in garments of green samite. He wore a beautiful sash of the same shade of green. The lady had worked it for him.

They flew into each other's arms. Like a well-bred lady, then she greeted him properly and welcomed him to her home. Together they sat on a low bench covered with tapestry. The lady began to tell him of her sorrow because she had to stay. She told it from beginning to end while he listened.

"Lady," he told her, "by God who moved mountains, I never have had such sorrow in my life as I have now because of leaving you." As he said it, he kissed her. The lady gently put her arms about him. After a moment he spoke to her again.

"My heart is wild with grief as the time to leave draws nearer. But I know well that wherever I am, my heart is yours. I could never be glad in any land whatsoever for thinking night and day only of you, for having you every moment in my memory, for thinking of when we will have our joy again. I shall take comfort in such thoughts, for I see that otherwise there will be no comfort for me. Such comforts will not fail me, nor such hopes ever change unless one of us dies before the season and the space when our departing ends. And for your love I will do such things which I will swear firmly, and I will make such a swearing that neither lady nor damsel shall my lips ever touch, no matter how sweet, nor how beautiful, nor how provocative she may be, neither out of flirtation nor of my seeking. I could do no such thing in any manner whatsoever, for my body goes forth from you . . . without its heart."

"Oh, my sweet love," the lady told him, "I swear to you and maintain upon my soul that I shall never rest until I

191

see you once more. And that when you depart from me, you will bear with you my heart, for it is all dutifully yours. But I believe that I shall not be able to last nor to live long since I was the one who caused you to go far from me. Alas! What a terrible pain it is! For near you I always had pleasure, relief, gayety, and the sweetest thoughts, and joy both evening and every morning long. Oh, what has happened to all that since I have lost you?" Suddenly the lady, even as she spoke those last words, fainted away from anguish. She choked on her words.

The Châtelain took her in his arms, her body twisted and hurting. He felt even greater pain, but he neither cried out nor wept. He only held her against him as close as he could and gave her many little, light kisses. Then he said to her, "My very sweet heart, comfort yourself. Don't cry any longer. When I see you bathed in your tears, lying here still in my arms, it breaks my heart and truly kills me unless you take comfort again."

When she regained consciousness she was like a wild woman. "Oh, what will become of me?" she cried. "Dear love, I am going to lose you!"

"Lady," said Isabelle. "This is no nice way to part. You should be struggling to comfort your love. Instead of this, you discomfort him all the more. On my soul, you do wrong. . . . Make your parting beautiful. Take heart and courage from a face that is glad and cheerful."

"Oh, Isabelle! How can I be cheerful? If you had the sorrow I have in your heart, you couldn't act happy nor even want to act happy."

"Beloved," the Châtelain told her, "try to be your usual self. Before you know it, I will be back from across the sea. And I give you my solemn oath that I shall never love another but you."

"Love," she said, "I want to give you a ring that I have especially loved, if you wish to keep it for me. And here are some strands of my hair that I want to cut for you."

"Oh, God," said the Châtelain, "Lady, on my soul, don't cut your hair for me. Please leave it."

"If you love me, you will carry them with you, and with you goes all my heart. And if without dying I could take it out, I would trust that to you, too."

Wandering about the room, the lady took scissors and cut several strands of her hair and twisted them tightly and wrapped them in sandalwood and gave them to him. He accepted the gift and promised that he would keep them for love of her and bring them back to her also.

They spent two days together, but they had little solace or joy because ever present in their minds was the thought that they had to part. When the time came, he took his leave. He was full of anger and wrath. He and Gobert left Fayel at once. They found the King of England at Marseilles where his navy was ready to put out to sea. God sent them such good winds that they arrived directly at Acre, which had been delivered.

In any history book can be found the story of King Richard's prowess in war, his gallantry towards his knights, and the fear he instilled in the Saracens. The Châtelain was in the forefront of the combats. He wore on his helmet the strands of his lady's hair which he had had interwoven with threads of pure gold. At his awesome aspect the enemy were terrified. They called him the Knight of Prowesses and the Knight of the Tresses.

He had been by King Richard for two long years when one day the Saracens attacked them in a small castle they held. The knights sallied forth, drove the enemy away, and were giving chase when the Châtelain's side was pierced to the depth of a palm by a *quarrel*, or triangular arrowhead. He could not stand in his stirrups. He fell fainting over the saddle. His companions stopped the pursuit in order to carry him inside the castle. King Richard, very grieved, called for doctors to come to him from all over the country.

The doctors gathered in consultation. They were the best in the world. They examined the wound and were able to draw out the arrow blade. They felt his body up and around, and then washed out the wound with sweet water. They advised King Richard that within twenty days the Châtelain would be healed and up and about. They added that if the arrowhead had been dipped in poison, however, that the knight would die, that he could not escape death, that no one could cure him.

The Châtelain lay many days without healing. He grew pale and thin. The doctors' remedies did him no good. His body wasted away. Gobert became more and more worried. The Châtelain complained often that it was only from absence that he languished and not from the wound. At such times he said he wanted to go home at once where he knew he would be cured. If he were at home, his lady would come to him. She would know how to restore his health. King Richard granted him leave to depart on a ship that was taking some cardinals and other dignitaries into Italy. The Châtelain and Gobert thus set sail for home.

At first the sea air and the thought of drawing nearer to his beloved seemed to revive the Châtelain, but very soon he was no longer even able to stand. Realizing that he had not long to live, he composed one last love song. This last poem was composed in severe pain and with trouble because the Châtelain did not have before his eyes the dear face of his lady. Then he called Gobert and asked if he would undertake to do his last bidding. With a sad and mournful heart Gobert agreed. He brought his master a little silver casket in which the golden tresses of the lady were kept. As the Châtelain turned them over in his fingers, he almost thought the strands of her hair were pure gold. "Alas," he sighed, "death will sever true lovers and faithful

194

ones like ourselves!" Then he sent Gobert to find a scholar on board who knew how to write cursively. To this learned person the Châtelain dictated his letter:

To you, my sweet and beloved Lady
Whose true love I have been
And whose servant also in all places
Whatsoever to the end of my life,
I address this last testament
Plentifully loving you and greeting you
Since as for me I seek nothing more.
Lady, I herewith give you notice
That I have been both morning and evening
Your man, your servant, your knight
Both utterly and faithfully until
This hour when I depart from you
For which I am all the more ill
And anguished inasmuch as I know
That never, no day, shall I see you again.
And because I know and believe
That I bore your heart with me
The day I left Fayel and
You gave me as a jewel which
Was most lovely and desired
Your noble and lustrous hair
Which I have guarded from that time,
I send you here enclosed my heart.
It is yours, and right for you to have it
So be quite certain that on no day
No true love died with sadder heart
Than I now die in such discomfort,
Since after my death I can never
Speak to you. It has been such a
Long time since our lips spoke!
Oh! sweet and gentle creature

Who defies all portraiture, Lady
Of such beauty, line and shape,
Your heart is a flawlessly formed
Gem, a sapphire, a crimson rose.
Most beautiful of all ladies,
Unequalled among living women
And the best among the better, provided
Superabundantly with goods and honors,
An example among women to shame
All the unknowing and those gone astray
From understanding, honor and virtue,
You of all goods the treasure and richness,
You, sweet fountain of pity,
Full and overflowing with goodness—
   Most noble and delicate Lady,
Blossom grafted on a flowering tree,
Now I am pain-wracked and torn
That you may never see me again
Nor I you, as was our wont.
Alas! now has all joy failed me
And when now I see that I must die
And that it cannot be otherwise
I pray to Almighty God
That He grant my soul salvation
And that when it is severed,
Yours too may be sent to mine,
Your soul and mine together
In heaven for our everlasting lives.

The Châtelain lost consciousness many times before he
was able to finish his letter. When it was done, he folded
it himself and affixed his seal. At once he had his signet
thrown overboard into the sea. Then he instructed his body
servant and Gobert to open his chest as soon as he was
dead, to take out his heart, to place it with the tresses and

the letter in the silver box, and to deliver the casket to the Lady of Fayel. He asked Gobert to comfort the lady, to reason her out of an excessive grief, and to say that he sent back her gift and his own remains along with the letter to her. Gobert put a little piece of bread in the Châtelain's mouth so he would find enough strength to complete his last instructions:

"It is my belief," said the Châtelain, "that there is a god on this earth, and that god is Love. He lives profusely in all lovers and cannot be dwindled. . . . Love was my sovereign who held me in his domain and rewarded me richly from the hour I entered the lady's service. If I cannot repay Love, let me praise him at least. Had I lived, I should have been faithful my whole life long. Love likes not a lover who takes back his heart for some task imposed upon him."

A cardinal heard the Châtelain's confession, administered the last sacrament, and gave him absolution. "Friend, have no fear, for you die in the work and in the service of Jesus Christ who created us and shaped us. Friend, keep the faith and abide by our laws. And I believe and know truly that you will be brought to salvation."

"Gobert," cried the Châtelain. "Greet milady for me." And he died. His orders were obeyed. When the ship landed in Italy, the Châtelain was interred there. Gobert set out at once for France with the silver casket. Through good weather and foul he trudged until he was only three leagues from Fayel. Then he took a by-road stealthily, hoping thus to arrive at the castle unseen. He had often taken this path in the days when he was the Lord of Fayel's squire. Gobert was unlucky.

There, before him on the path—too late to turn aside— was the Lord of Fayel grimacing with anger and hatred. "How dare you set foot on my land when you and your master have so dishonored me? What are you tring to do —carry a message or a letter? By God, you have struck it wrong today. I shall hang you with my own hands."

In exchange for his life Gobert had to give the casket to the Lord of Fayel, had to tell him about the Châtelain's death. Then the lord ordered him off his lands immediately and forbade him ever to approach them again. The lord read the letter without breaking the seal and rode home laughing.

He instructed his master cook to prepare a fine dinner with jellies and capons and to make a special dish to be served to the lady alone—and to put in this dish the Châtelain's heart. . . . The tablecloths were spread. Supper was served in the most elegant manner. The dishes were delicious. The lady complimented her husband on the dish he had ordered for her. She said she had never tasted anything so delicious. "Why and how is it our cooks do not prepare this meat more often?"

"Lady, do not be amazed," her husband replied," that it is so delicious. One could not buy its like for any sum."

"What is it called, dear Sir? For the love of me, tell its name."

"Don't be so curious, Lady. I guarantee you in good faith that in this delicious viand you are eating the heart you love the most in the world—that served up to you of the Châtelain of Coucy. You loved him in his lifetime. For my revenge I have made you eat his heart."

Despite her great fright, the lady kept her wits about her. "Surely, Sir, I cannot believe that such words are true. He has not been seen in our country for two years now—not since he took the cross and went overseas."

"Hand me the casket," the lord ordered a valet. "Now I will show her if I speak a lie or the truth." He showed her the tresses. He read her the letter from beginning to end. He asked her if she recognized the seal. "Lady, believe without any doubt, that you have eaten his heart. You may be certain of it."

"By God, Sire," she answered. "That grieves me, and since it is true, I guarantee you certainly that on no day shall I eat again nor shall I ever take another morsel after so gentle a meat. My life is now too heavy a burden for me to bear. I do not wish to live longer. Death, deliver me from my life!"

As she finished speaking, the lady fell forward, her head on the table. Her pain was so sharp that none of her limbs, none of her veins, had any strength in them. Her servants lifted her and placed her limp on her bed. There she lay as if lifeless. Her pain made all pale, all tainted. Some time later she opened her eyes.

"Oh, what has happened to me? Lord God, what have I become? Now can I protest and say: 'Lover!' When I lost my sweet love who was so honest and so self-effacing, loyal, and secret above all men—that even in all France and all Germany there was not such an one! What maddens me is that I intrigued like a fool to send him overseas. . . . Since he is dead, for what should I live? How sad he was when he sent me his heart. How well he showed me he was mine. My heart was his, and is now. I will show how I shall end for his love. . . ." She spoke no more—only aroused from time to time to twist her hands and tear her flesh. She was so frantic that her eyes rolled back in her head. Death was already near her. She lived barely any longer—only prayed God to take her swiftly and release her soul from her body. She lay lifeless. Oh, may God have pity on her!

Her husband was moved, overcome with anger and grief to see how quickly she had died. For fear of reprisals, he gave her a fine funeral. When her relatives heard what had happened, they said he had murdered her. Why pause over all that? The relatives were appeased only when the Lord of Coucy went overseas. He came back too. But he never smiled again. He died soon after his return. . . .

199

True love lies halfway between sadness and joy. Its fevers are like the fires of a blacksmith's forge. When the smith kindles his fire and blows upon it so he can hammer the red hot iron on his anvil, then he throws water upon it without extinguishing the fire. . . . Such is love, which blows one hour hot and the next hour cold. It is an unquenchable fire. No one can enumerate the pangs with which a lover is pained, nor either the joy, nor the delight he feels by day, nor the delight he feels by night.

IX

THE ROMANCE OF THE STORY OF THE GRAIL

Robert de Boron

THIRTEENTH CENTURY

VERY SINNER, every small man, every smaller must know how before Jesus Christ came upon the earth His coming had been announced and proclaimed by prophets; that God would send His son upon the earth to suffer many torments, many sorrows, much cold, and much heat. In those days, when my story takes place, kings, princes, dukes, counts, our first father and mother—Adam and Eve—Abraham, Isaac, Jacob, Jeremiah, the prophet Isaiah, every prophet, all other people both good and evil alike went straight to hell when they departed from that century. When ugly devils had kicked them into hell, they trusted and believed that they had won. . . . The good, however, still took comfort in the

Son of God, whom they awaited whenever it should be pleasing to Our Lord to do us that great honor of having Him descend upon the earth in human flesh and human likeness.

He overshadowed her.* He formed her as He wished her to be—simple, sweet, well taught—and made for His intent. Filled with all goodnesses. Highly favored with all beauties.† She was as rich with flowers as the honeysuckle vine. She was also as a rose in bloom, for she bore the sweet rose in bud . . . its petals closed inside her body. . . . And her name was Mary. . . . § Illumined was she with all brightnesses. . . . Mary meaning sea, meaning mother. Mary . . . daughter and mother of God.

God wished His Son to become flesh of the Virgin and to be born of her, and He did this as He was pleased to do, and it was to her according to His word.** Our Lord who took His humanness from her showed His tender mercy upon us when He descended upon earth to die for our sake because He wished to salvage the labors of His Father and deliver us out of the hands of our enemies to whom Eve had betrayed us. . . . Eve ate of the forbidden fruit and gave also to her husband and he ate.‡ Then they were ashamed of their nakedness. For this disobedience was their pain multiplied and in severe pain Eve brought forth her children. But God sent His Son to give knowledge of salvation unto His people in the remission of their sins.§§ To save the works of His Father, Jesus suffered bitter death. For this task He assumed the burden of life in the womb of the Virgin Mary and then was born in Bethlehem of the Virgin, just as I say. . . . This thing is grievously hard for

* Luke 1:35.
† Luke 1:28.
§ Luke 1:27.
** Luke 1:38.
‡ Genesis 3.
§§ Luke 1:77.

me to tell, for the fountainhead of the Virgin's blessedness is overflowing and inexhaustibly so, but I must quench my words and come back to my story inasmuch as I have memory of it and health and power within myself to tell it.

In the time when God walked upon the earth and preached His teachings, the land of Judaea was under Rome, and to Rome was answerable that part of it where Pilate ruled. The enemies of Jesus were all assembled, and to them Judas betrayed Him. Among their number was a certain Joseph of Arimathea* who was not proud to be of their company, but he knew how Jesus would be betrayed by one of the twelve. . . . And so He was betrayed by the kiss of Judas and taken. And the cup from which He drank at the Last Supper, the cup which was the new covenant in His blood, was found in Simon's house and kept.

When they brought Jesus to trial, Pilate called for water and before them washed his hands saying that thus his hands were cleansed and washed and he was quit and innocent of their judgment since he found no fault in the prisoner. The man who kept the cup gave it secretly to Pilate.

When Joseph of Arimathea heard of Jesus's death, he was full of sorrow and wrath. He hurried to Pilate. "I and my fine knights have served you long without wages or reward. Give me the gift you have promised. Give it to me. You have the power."

"Only ask," Pilate answered. "I will give you what you wish. You have deserved great rewards."

"Sire," said Joseph, "my thanks! I ask for the body of Jesus whom they wrongfully hanged upon the cross."

Marveling greatly that Joseph should ask for such a trifle, Pilate said, "I thought in my heart that you would wish a greater thing and certainly you would have received

* Luke 23:51; Mark 15:43.

it. Inasmuch as you ask for this body, you shall have it as your wages. . . . Go take it at once."*

When Joseph went to the cross and saw Jesus hanging there so vilely, he began to weep from pity. He said to the guards who were there, "Pilate gave me this body, told me and commanded me to withdraw it from this spite."

All together they replied, "Do not withdraw it, for He has said that on the third day He will rise from the dead. If you touch Him, we will kill you."

Again Joseph returned to Pilate who this time ordered Nicodemus to accompany Joseph. Then Pilate took out the cup when he remembered. He recalled Joseph and gave it to him. "You loved that man dearly."

"You have spoken truly," answered Joseph.

Then, despite protests from the crowd, Joseph and Nicodemus climbed up and drew the body from the cross. Joseph took it in his arms and softly laid it on the ground. Gently he turned it and bathed it. As he cared for it, he saw fresh blood begin to flow from the wounds. Then he ran for his cup and gathered in it the drops of blood as best he could. Then he wrapped the body in cloth he had bought and laid it on a stone and covered it with a slab which we here call a tomb. Then Joseph went home while the armed enemies mounted guard about the tomb.

When despite the guards Jesus did arise from the dead and did appear again to his disciples, the enemies burst open the gates to Joseph's *hôtel*. They allowed him to rise and dress. Then they seized him. When they interrogated Joseph as to the whereabouts of Jesus, the rich man replied, "When I placed him in the monument I left him to your knights and returned home. God knows I have not heard speak of him since."

"You stole him away."

* John 19:38; Matthew 27:57-60.

"I did not, in truth."

"He is not there where you put Him. Tell us where He is."

"I don't know where He is, if He is not where I put Him four days ago."

They took Joseph to the home of a rich man where they struck him and beat him. Inside was a round tower high and deep. There they threw him down flat to the bottom of the well in the deepest, darkest, and most horrible dungeon all made of hard rock. There they enclosed him and sealed up the stone and walled up the tower and barred it with heavy locks.

God did not forget one who suffered for Him. Into the prison He went bearing his cup, which shed a great white light into the darkness. When Joseph saw its rays, he rejoiced. He was filled with the grace of the Holy Ghost. "Lord and Almighty God," he asked, "whence comest such light?"

"Joseph, do not be dismayed. In you is the power of God which will save you and lead you into paradise.

> *Par fame estoit hons adirez,*
> *Et par fame fu recouvrez;*
> *Fame la mort nous pouchaça.*
> *Fame vie nous restora;*
> *Par fame estions emprisonné.*
> *Par fame fumes recouvré.*

"Man was lost through woman—and through woman was recovered. Woman purchased death for us, and a woman restored us to life. Through woman were we emprisoned and through a woman were recovered."

"How, Sire?" Joseph asked. "Are you then Jesus who took on flesh in the precious Virgin?"

"I am He in truth. Believe it, and you will have everlasting life. So far you have loved me in secret, but the day will come when love of me will be open and when everyone can know it. . . . You will keep this cup for me and entrust its care only to three persons. You will take it in the name of the Father, and of the Son, and of the Holy Ghost. And you will believe that they are each one and the same. . . . Joseph, you know how I ate the Last Supper on a Thursday in Simon's house and how the wine represented my blood and how the cup shall be called chalice. . . . You shall remain here in prison and in darkness. Take care not to fear nor to have sadness in your heart, for those who shall hear of your deliverance will call it a marvel. The Holy Ghost will be with you and comfort you."

Thus Joseph remained a long time in prison. No one spoke of him any more until one day certain pilgrims who had seen Christ working miracles traveled from Judaea to Rome. There they lodged at a nobleman's house. The emperor's son at Rome was afflicted with leprosy. His body was so vile and so stinking that no one could abide him. They had walled him in a tower where there was neither gate nor window, only a narrow fenestella where they could push in a dish when they fed him. The pilgrims learned of Vespasian's illness. Then they told of Jesus, His miracles and His death. In their opinion, had Jesus lived and had He so desired, He could have healed Vespasian.

"Would you dare say and retrace before Caesar what you have told me?" asked their Roman host.

"Yes, in truth," they replied. As warranty that they spoke only the truth, the pilgrims asked to be put under lock and key until the emperor's wisest investigator from Rome could journey east to corroborate their testimony. Word was also sent to Pilate that if the pilgrims' account of Jesus's crucifixion was true, then he could expect the worst.

Pilate met Caesar's envoy in Arimathea. Without dismounting, he read the letters addressed to him from Rome.

He dared not rejoice. "I have read the letters," said Pilate. "I am familiar with the circumstances therein related."

Everyone marveled at his admission. This could be folly on his part. This could lead to his death. Behind closed doors Pilate himself told the whole story of Jesus's life and death. "Powerful men required me to condemn him," he said. "I told them I could not pass sentence, for I saw no reason to do so. . . . My knight Joseph took down the prophet's body, but despite inquiries I have not been able to ascertain what happened to Joseph." The envoy did not find in Pilate as much guilt as he had expected. For a month a search was made throughout Judaea. Nothing important was discovered. Then an assembly of notables was called. There Pilate's story was corroborated.

"Could you tell us," inquired the envoy, "if there is anything left that belonged to Jesus? Is there anything that we could carry to Rome? We should very much like to find some evidence."

One of them knew a woman who had a likeness which she adored every day. Further inquiry revealed that the woman's name was Verrine and that she lived in the Street of the School. Pilate summoned her. When she came before him, Pilate rose. The poor woman was amazed at the deference he showed her. At first the woman denied that she had such a likeness, but when the envoy explained that the emperor hoped it would cure his son Vespasian and when he pressed her to sell it, she answered, "I would not sell it for anything at all, nor would I give it. I will upon your guarantee travel to Rome with you and carry it with me."

The old woman returned to her home and hiding the likeness under her coat took it to Pilate's court. All rose in her Presence. "Be seated," she said, "and you will see this cloth which wiped the face of God." As soon as they saw it, they rose to their feet and asked her to tell them how she came by it. "I will tell you," she answered. "I had ordered

208

some cloth. I was carrying it home in my arms when I met the prophet right on the road I was going. His hands were tied with thongs behind His back. The Jews whom I met prayed me in God's name to lend them my cloth to wipe His face. I took my cloth and dried His face myself. I went home, and they took Him away. When I got inside, I looked at my cloth. On it I saw His image just as you see it now. If you think it may cure the emperor's son, then I will take it to him willingly."

As soon as the cloth stamped with the face of Jesus was held up before the fenestella, Vespasian was instantly cured. The image became a holy relic at Rome where it was called the *Veronica* in honor of the woman who had used it.

Vespasian set out at once for Judaea where he also exonerated Pilate but executed thirty Jews whom he inculpated. Other executions followed until one man offered in exchange for his life information about Joseph of Arimathea. Thus Vespasian found the dungeon in which Joseph had been walled up alive. Vespasian had the capstone removed. He looked down the black shaft and called. There was no answer. The Jews said it would be a marvel if the prisoner still lived, for he had been there so long without eating or drinking or having any care. Vespasian replied that he would not believe him dead until he had seen it with his own eyes. He asked for a long rope. He called down the shaft again and again. There was no reply. He had the cord dropped towards an area where he thought he saw a certain glimmering of light. Then he slid down the cord.

When Joseph saw Vespasian, he said, "Welcome, Vespasian. What do you wish?"

Vespasian marveled to hear himself so addressed. "Who told you my name?" he asked. "You didn't answer when I called. Therefore I came down here. Tell me on your life, who are you?"

"I am Joseph," he said, "of Arimathea."

"Thank God for having saved you. We should never have done it without Him." Then Vespasian and Joseph clasped each other in their arms and embraced each other from love.

"Joseph, who told you my name?"

"He who told me the whole world."

Then Vespasian told how he had been cured.

"Of what illness?" Joseph asked.

"Of leprosy."

"Vespasian, it was the Holy Ghost which shaped all things—all sky, all earth, all sea. It made the nights, the days, the elements, and the four winds. It made and created the archangels and made altogether the bands of angels. . . ." Joseph it was who instructed Vespasian into the teachings of Jesus and who converted him.

Joseph had a sister named Enygeus and a brother-in-law named Hebron or Brons. Both loved Joseph dearly. When they heard he was alive, they went to see him at once. Joseph told them he lived through no merit of his own. "It was due to the Lord, son of the most sainted maiden Mary, handmaid* of the lord. . . . If you will believe in me do not remain here any longer. Leave your inheritance, your lands, and your lodgings. We shall go together into exile. We shall bear all for the love of God."

Vespasian took revenge for the death of Jesus whom he loved. Joseph took leave of him and departed from that land. He led his people with him. They went away into distant lands where they resided a long time. In these new places Joseph taught all he knew. He taught them how to cultivate the fields. The people prospered. For many years they lacked nothing. After a while, however, things went badly for them. Whatever they did, however hard they labored night and day, things went badly. Finally they

* Luke 1:38. (*ancele* as in *l'ancele* or *l'ancelot*.)

went to Hebron. They asked him to consult Joseph for them.

Weeping, Joseph knelt before the chalice. "Lord," he prayed, "You commanded me when You gave me this cup that whenever I needed Your aid I was to come before this sacred vessel where Your glorious blood is and pray to You and beseech Your counsel. The people lack bread and meat. Tell them how to work Your pleasure and accomplish Your will."

"Joseph," said the voice, "you will take this vessel which contains my blood and you will put it to the test. Once before, this cup discovered the sinner. He alone drew back from it. You will summon your brother-in-law Brons, who is a good man. You will have him go out into this water and catch a fish. Have him bring to you the first one he catches. And do you know what you will do? You will put it on this table and beside it the cup, just as I was seated before it at the Last Supper. Seat Brons on your right hand. Then all will see how Brons will draw back from the empty chair. That seat cannot be filled until Brons has a child from his wife. . . . Then ask your people to be seated at the table."

Joseph obeyed the commandments to the letter. Certain among the people took seats at the table. Others abstained. The table was entirely filled except for that seat which could not be occupied; those who sat down to eat received promptly into their hearts a sweetness and the fulfillment of their desires. Those who felt a state of grace generally put out of mind the others who showed no signs of it.

One of those seated, a man named Peter, looked behind him and saw those who were standing by stolidly. Very meekly he inquired, "Tell me. Can you neither feel nor know anything of what we feel?"

They replied, "Nothing."

"Then none of us," he replied, "can help but suspect that you are in the snares of the sin Joseph warned us of—the sin of lust. This is the reason why you have fallen from grace."

The wretched sinners for shame stole out of the room. One of them was weeping. As soon as the services were over, the others joined them. Joseph advised his worshipers to return every day. . . . In this way, by direct demonstration from Almighty God, was Joseph able to perceive and to know the sinners from the righteous. The chalice was beloved after this first test of its power.

Those who had remained away from the table kept inquiring, "What do you think of this 'grace'? What do you think it does to you? Who gave you this gift? Who informed you of it?"

Peter answered, "It comes from blessed Jesus, He who saved Joseph from the prison where he had been so unjustly cast."

"What is the reputation your chalice will have in the world?" they asked. "Tell us more about it. What name will you call it when you name it by its real name?"

"I care not to conceal its name. He who has acquired that right may rightfully call it by its real name. He will call it the Grail. I do believe that we shall never be able to see it unless the Grail so permits us to do. It makes pleasant, prosperous, and comely all those who are allowed to remain in its circle and all those who may use its power. They are as adroit as the fish which a man holds in his hand and sees twist out of his fingers and leap back into deep water."

The cup or chalice was thereafter only hailed by its proper name—that of the Grail. Not only those who stayed at the table but also those who departed named it the Grail, for the reason I have stated. Those people who remained celebrated undernsong at the tierce hour or at 9:00 A.M. in honor of the Grail. This was its service. And also this is why I call my work *The Story of the Grail;* for this name it shall have from that time to this.

Those disbelieving people who went away left one of their number behind them, a man named Moses, who seemed very crafty, very tricky about himself, very tortuous of speech. From start to finish he gave the appearance of knowledge and goodheartedness. He said he would not frequent folks who had lost the grace of the Holy Ghost. Whenever anyone passed beside Moses, he prayed loudly for grace and sobbed and pleaded that he be brought before Joseph and that he be pitied. Then in 'a small voice he kept urging in the most humble manner, "In God's name, ask Joseph to obtain grace for me." He was so insistent that finally certain men decided to intervene on his behalf.

"It is not mine to give," Joseph replied.

"Sire, we have confidence in Moses," they said.

(After Moses had knelt before the Grail, the voice said, "If he is what he pretends to be, let him step forward and take a seat at the table. Then you will see what becomes of him." Then to his sponsors the voice added, "Tell Moses that if he is such as should receive grace, then no one can take it from him; if he is otherwise than he seems, let him not approach; for he can never deceive others nor betray others so disastrously as he can do to himself."

When Moses heard this, he boasted, "I am not afraid of anything so long as I have Joseph's permission to approach. Let him not think that I am such as should not draw near."

"You have his leave," they said, "so long as you obey the laws." Then they took him between them and escorted him to the service.

Joseph, seeing Moses approach, said, "Moses, Moses, do not draw nearer to this if you are unworthy. You can never deceive us as you can deceive yourself. Take care that you are the man people assume you are."

"Since I am truly good," he answered, "let God permit me to remain in your society."

"Step forward then. We shall see if you are what you say you are."

Then Joseph, Brons, and the others sat around the table.

213

When they were seated, Moses circled about them fearfully but could find no place except that one nearest Joseph. Therefore he sat down. No sooner was he seated than he melted into the earth so completely that it seemed he had never existed. The others were terribly frightened to see a man destroyed right in their midst.

"Tell us what happened to Moses," Peter asked Joseph.

"I have no idea," he replied. "If it pleases Him, we shall know it and more." Alone and kneeling before the Grail, he asked, "God, as manifold are Your works, . . .)* show me what happened to Moses that I may instruct my people."

Appearing to Joseph, the voice answered, "Now the meaning should be clear to you when I say that you founded this table so that one seat should be reserved in memory of Judas who lost his place from ignorance even when I foretold his betrayal. This seat shall not be filled until Judgment Day, which all men await. For your comfort I say that it will be filled on earth but not until the third man shall have sprung from your stock. Hebron will engender him by way of Joseph's sister Enygeus. The one who will be born from her son is the man who will sit in this place.

"As for Moses, he remained behind the others in order to trick you. Know in truth that he has melted into the abyss and there is lost. He shall never be remembered in fable or song until he who fills up the void shall have come."

"Great is the majesty of God," Joseph told his people, "and foolish is he who pursues foolish ways in this vale of sorrow."

Brons and his wife lived a long life. Twelve sons were born to them, twelve handsome, gentle, and strapping boys. When they were grown, Enygeus asked her husband Joseph as to their future. An angel gave the answer. "If they

* There is a *lapsus* in the manuscript here.

wish to marry, then let them. If one does not wish to take a wife, then the married men will serve that one."

It came to pass, even as the angel had predicted, that one of the twelve did not wish to have a wife. His father asked this boy, "Son, why do you not wish to marry as your brothers have done?"

"Do not mentioned marriage to me," he said. "I shall never have a wife nor wed any woman as long as I live."

This son Alein was entrusted to Joseph, who made him his heir and the chieftain of the family. The boy was taught the life of Jesus, the sufferings of Joseph, and how to guard the Grail. He was told that a male child would be his and that he should go into the Occident, even into the farthest western land that there was. The boy was also to be present when orders from the Grail were divulged to Peter, who would elect to go to the Valley of Avalon, there to settle. Those lands, indeed, faced west. There they would await further instructions from the son named Alein.

If Master Robert de Boron were to set down here all the teachings Joseph taught his nephew Alein, he would have to double his story two hundred times at least. . . . Suffice it to say that when Alein had learned all the big books by heart and had become converted, he was returned to his parents. They made him their heir and lord of his brothers and sisters who paid him homage.

Peter elected to go to the Valley of Avalon, a very savage country that lay all the way to the west. Alein also led his brothers and sisters into strange lands where to all he met he told of Jesus and His story. The care of the Grail was entrusted by Joseph to Brons, for he had been the man good enough to catch the fish. In the future Brons was to be designated by his real name—The Rich Fisherman. In sign of the Trinity the Grail would descend from Brons to Alein to his son.

Thus the Rich Fisherman came into the possession of

the Grail and its marvelous powers. Brons set out towards the west with Joseph accompanying him for the first three days of his journey. The Rich Fisherman became world famous. Countless tales were told about him in the western land where he settled. Master Robert de Boron told about his son Alein, what happened to him, what lands he ruled, and what lady he took, and what heirs he had. Master Robert also wrote about Peter and told what happened to Moses who was lost so long. These four separate stories— of the Rich Fisherman, of Alein, of Peter, and of Moses— needed to be told apart from each other and yet in the same book. No man could tell them, of course, if he had not first heard *Of the Grail The* very great *Story*, a story which is entirely true.

In the days when I told it I was living in peacetime with my lord, Gautier de Mont Belyal. Before my days no mortal man ever told this tale.

I hereby say to whom it may concern, that those who wish to have the sequels to this story may find them in my next book insomuch as God gives me health, life, good fortune, and the will power to assemble the material.

X

AUCASSIN AND NICOLETTE

Anonymous

THIRTEENTH CENTURY

 HO would like to hear some good verses made up for the delight of an old prisoner about two beautiful little youngsters, Nicolette and Aucassin, about the great pains he endured and the deeds of prowess he did for his sweetheart of the lovely face? . . . Sweet are the verses and beautiful the prose, courtly and well connected. No man is so scatterbrained, however sad or busy he may be, however sick of an old sickness, that if he but hear them he will be cured and transported with joy— so sweet and over-sweet is this story.

Now they say and they tell and they write also that Count Bougars of Valence was making war on Count Garins de Biaucaire—such a great war and so amazing a war and such a deadly war that not a single day passed but there he was at the gates and at the walls and at the barricades to the city, with a hundred and with a thousand thousand foot soldiers and cavalry; so he burned the crops and he laid waste the countryside and his men were slaughtered. Count Garins de Biaucaire was old and frail and had overstayed his time. He had no descendant, neither son nor daughter, except one youngster who was such as I shall tell you.

The young lord's name was Aucassin. He was handsome and gentlemanly, tall and with well-proportioned legs and feet and body and arms. His hair was blond and it curled into small ringlets on his head. His eyes were a blue-green, and laughing eyes they were. His face was open and easily read. His nose was arched and prominent. Aucassin was so made up of good features that he had not a single bad one, or if one was bad, it would have looked good on him. . . . *But* he had been caught napping by "Love" which "conquers all," to such a degree that he wouldn't become a knight, nor take arms, nor go joust, nor do what he ought to when he ought.

His father and mother used to reason with him. "Son, for . . . take arms! Get on your horse! Defend your lands! Have your own combatants! If they see you among them, they will be more inclined to defend themselves and their possessions, and your lands, and mine."

"Father," said Aucassin, "what are you talking about now? You know God doesn't give me anything I ask Him for. What would be the point of my being a knight and mounting a war horse or riding off to storm or to war where I'd pierce somebody or he'd pierce me unless you give me my sweetheart Nicolette whom I love so!"

"Son," said the father, "that could not be. Leave Nicolette be! Because she's a prisoner who was brought here from a foreign country so the viscount of this city bought her from the Saracens and brought her to this city. What if he did have her baptized and make her his goddaughter!

218

What if he does give her some bachelor knight who will earn bread honorably for her! That's none of your concern. If you want to get married, I'll give you the daughter of a king or of a count. There isn't a man in France, and I don't care how rich he is, but if you want his daughter you can have her."

"Oh, stop it, father," said Aucassin. "Where is there any honor in land so high that if my sweetheart Nicolette had it would not be well settled upon her? If she were the empress of Constantinople or the empress of Germany, or the queen of France or the queen of England, that would be little enough for her, so noble is she and so courteous and so high-born and so featured with good features."

. . . No one could make Aucassin retract his preference, which his father did not allow. Sometimes his mother threatened him. "Oh my goodness, false son! What's the matter with you? Nicolette is gay and adorable, but she was cast out of Carthage and bought by a Saxon. If you want to take a wife, then choose one with high connections."

"Mother, I can not do it. Nicolette is of high birth. Her gentle body and her face and her beauty lighten my heart. It is only right that I have her love, which is so sweet."

—When Count Garins de Biaucaire saw that he could not divert his son Auccassin from loving Nicolette, he rode down to the viscount of that city who was his vassal and he called him to task. "Sir Viscount," he said, "get your god-daughter Nicolette out of here. May the land from which she was brought into this country be accursed! It's on her account that I am losing Aucassin, who won't become a knight or do anything he ought to do. And furthermore, you may as well know that if I can get my hands on her, I'll burn her alive in a bonfire, and as for you, you can fear for yourself and everything else."

"Sire," answered the viscount, "I don't give a damn where he goes, or where he comes, or who he talks to. I bought her with my own money, and so I brought her up and I had her baptized and I made her my goddaughter. And I have planned to give her some bachelor knight who can earn her bread honorably. Now, none of this is any business of your son's. However, since such is according to your will and your advantage, I'll send her away into such a land and such a country as she shall never set eyes upon him again."

"See that you do it," said Count Garins. "Otherwise great misfortunes could come upon you."

The two men parted. Now this viscount was a wealthy man who therefore owned a rich palace behind a sloping garden. He had Nicolette shut up in an upper-story chamber where she was guarded by an old woman as her only companion and society. He had bread and wine taken to them and whatever else was necessary. Then he had the chamber door permanently sealed so that no one could either exit nor enter. Aside from this one door there was only a window overlooking the garden, just a rather narrow window through which there came up to them a little fresh air.

. . . Thus Nicolette was emprisoned in a vaulted room which had been beautifully decorated and painted with flowers. The maiden sat leaning on the marble window ledge. . . . She had blond hair and arched eyebrows. Her face was open, her skin fair. You never saw a prettier girl. She sat looking over the full-blown roses and into the forest. She told the little singing birds how she was an orphan.

"Oh, my," she said. "Alas! I am a captive. Why was I put into prison? Aucassin, Sire, young lord, it is only because I am your sweetheart and only because you don't despise me! I have been shut up in prison because of you, where in this vaulted chamber I drag out my miserable life. But, in the name of God the son of Mary, I shall not stay here long if I can help it."

—Nicolette was there in her prison, in the chamber, as

you have heard and understood. Meanwhile the word and the heralding went out all over the land and that country to the effect that Nicolette had been lost. Some had it that she had managed to escape from the land; others said that Count Garins de Biaucaire had caused her to be put to death. Whoever may have been joyful because of this, Aucassin was not happy. He went to the viscount of the city and asked for an explanation.

"Sire Viscount," he said, "what have you done with my sweetheart Nicolette, that person whom I loved more than the whole world? Have you taken her away from me? Have you hidden her somewhere? Know that if you cause my death, your good faith will come into question. That will only be rightful, for it will be just as if you strangled me with your two hands. What you will have done is deprive me of what I loved best in all the world."

"Fine Sire," said the viscount. "Let it alone. Nicolette is a captive whom I purchased abroad. So what if I bought her out of my own money, and raised her, had her baptized and stood godfather to her, and fed her, and one of these days would have given her a young bachelor who could have earned her bread honorably! None of that is any concern of yours. Why don't you marry the daughter of a king or a count? Besides all that, what do you expect to have gained when you have made her your mistress and put her in your bed? You would not have conquered very much when every day of the century your soul would then be going into hell and when you could never, never enter paradise."

"What do I care about paradise? I don't want to enter it. I only wish to have Nicolette whom I love so. Nobody goes to paradise except such people as I shall name for you. Old priests go there, old clodhoppers, and one-arms who all day and all night crouch before the altars in old crypts, old fellows with threadbare cloaks and old tattered clothes, all naked and shoeless, and tumored old folks who are dying anyway of hunger and thirst, cold and disease. All those go to paradise, and I don't give a damn about them because I myself want to go to hell.

"To hell go the fine intellectuals, and the handsome knights dead in tournaments and gallant wars, and good soldiers and fine fellows. I want to go with them. And into hell go the lovely ladies of courtly life who have had, each one of them, two or three lovers along with their own barons. And there also go the golden-haired and the silver, and the blue-eyed and the gray, and there also go the minstrels and the jugglers and the king troubadours of the century. I want to go with them, but first let me have Nicolette, my very sweetheart, with me."

"For certain," said the viscount, "you are wasting your words, for you shall never see her again. And if you were to speak to her and your father knew it, he would burn both me and her in a bonfire, and you yourself would have plenty to fear."

"That deeply worries me," replied Aucassin. Then sadly he left the viscount.

. . . Aucassin went away sad and downcast because of his fair-faced love. No one could comfort him. No one could give him good counsel. He went home to his palace, climbed the stairs, entered his chamber, and began to weep and abandon himself to great sorrow and lament for his love.

"Nicolette, how beautiful it was! What beautiful comings and goings! What beautiful times we had and what beautiful words! What beautiful meetings and beautiful games! What beautiful kisses! What beautiful embraces! It is for you that I am grief stricken, and so manhandled that I don't think I can live through it."

While Aucassin was in his chamber lamenting the loss of his sweetheart Nicolette, Count Bougars of Valence did not forget to pursue his war. On the contrary, he called up infantrymen and horsemen and set siege to the castle. The alarm was sounded. A cry was raised. Knights and sergeants leaped to their armor and arms and rushed to doors and ramparts to defend the castle. Burgesses climbed up to the battlements where they began to hurl down stones and sharpened stakes. While the assault was heavy and in full force, Count Garins de Biaucaire went into Aucassin's chamber where the boy was grieving and mourning for his sweetheart Nicolette whom he loved so.

"Ha, son!" he said. "What a most wretched coward you are, when you see that all the strongest and the best are assaulting your own castle! I want you to know one thing —that if you lose it, you shall be disinherited. Son, why, go take your weapons. Get on your horse. Defend your birthright. Have your men follow. Go into the fight. You will never strike a man nor the others you, but, if your men see you among them, they will better defend their possessions and their lives, and your lands and mine. You are so tall now and so strong that you can do it, and you ought to do it."

"Father," Aucassin said, "What are you talking about now? Already God doesn't give me a thing I ask Him for. If I were a knight, or mounted my horse, or went into the battle, when I pierced a knight there or others pierced me, what would be the use, unless you give me Nicolette, my sweetheart whom I love so!"

"Son," his father said, "this cannot be. Before I would allow myself to do your desires, I would lose whatever I have rather than let you have her as your woman or as your wife." He turned to leave. When Aucassin saw that he was going, he called him back.

"Father," said Aucassin, "come here. I'll make you a bargain."

"What bargain, fair son?"

"I will take up arms. I will go into battle on your word

that if God brings me back safe and sound you will let me see my sweetheart Nicolette long enough to have two or three words with her and long enough to have one kiss."

"Granted," said his father. When he allowed it, Aucassin was delighted.

. . . Aucassin heard of the kiss he would have on his return. He would not have been as happy if he had been offered a hundred thousand marks of pure gold. He called for his trappings forthwith, and they outfitted him. He donned a lined hauberk, laced his helmet upon his head, buckled on his sword with its fine gold hilt, mounted his war horse, took his shield and his pike, and looked down at his feet to see they were well set in the stirrups. He rode forth magnificently. As he spurred his horse forward, he was remembering his love. Willingly he galloped straight towards the gate and the thick of the battle.

—Thus, just as you have heard, Aucassin armed himself for battle and mounted his charger. God! How well his shield became his neck, and the helmet his head! How well his sword hung on his left hip! For the youngster was tall and strong and handsome and noble and well-equipped. And the horse he rode was powerful and swift. And the youngster brought him up smartly there at the gate.

Don't you think for one minute, however, that he was plotting to catch bulls or cows or rabbits, or that he would strike down some knight or that some knights would run at him. Not a bit of it. He didn't remember such things at all. He only thought so hard about Nicolette that he forgot the reins and whatever else he was supposed to do. And once the horse had felt the spurs, it carried him forth into the throng and bore him forward right into the middle of the enemy, which raised hands against him from all sides so that they captured him, stripped him of his lance and his shield, carried him off tightly pressed among them and were already discussing among themselves how they would put him to death, when all of a sudden Aucassin heard them.

"Oh, God," he said, "Oh, sweet creature! Are these my mortal enemies who are leading me along to cut off my head? Because if I get my head cut off, I shall never again speak to my Nicolette whom I love so. Now I still have my good sword, and I am still seated on my fresh charger. If I don't defend myself for her sake, never may God help her to love me again."

The youngster was tall and strong, and the horse he rode was mettlesome. So he put his hand to his sword and began to strike right and left, cut helmets and nosepieces and gauntlets and arms and make a carnage about him just as a wild boar does when the dogs close with him in the forest. Aucassin unhorsed ten knights, wounded seven, and undauntedly cut a path through the foe and went, sword in hand, galloping towards home through their ranks.

Since Count Bougars of Valence had heard that they were about to hang his enemy Aucassin, he was just riding in that direction. Aucassin did not fail to recognize him. He already held his sword raised. He struck him such a blow flat on the helmet that he crumpled it about his skull. The count was so stunned that he fell to the ground. Aucassin reached down, grabbed him, and taking him by the nosepiece of his helmet, dragged him to his father.

"Father," said Aucassin, "here is your enemy who wages such war and commits so many ill deeds against you. For twenty years this war, which no man before could ever stop, has lasted."

"Fine son," his father said, "such exploits are more like the youthful deeds of a hero—not gaping after some folly."

"Father," Aucassin replied, "don't go around any more preaching to me. Just keep your side of our bargain!"

"Bah! What bargain, fine son?"

"What! Father, have you forgotten it? Upon my head,

whoever may forget it, it lies so near and dear to my heart that I certainly won't forget. Did you not make a pact with me when I took arms and went into battle, that if God brought me back safe and sound you would let me see my sweetheart Nicolette long enough to exchange two words with her, or three, and that I would be able to kiss her once? Indeed, that is the very bargain you made with me, and my wish now is to see that you keep it."

"I did that?" said his father. "So help me God if I ever keep a bargain with you! And if she were here right now, I would burn her alive and give you plenty of cause to shake in your boots, too."

"Is that your last word?" asked Aucassin.

"So help me God," said his father. "Yes."

"For sure," said Aucassin, "now I am really sad when a man of your years is a liar! . . . Count of Valence," he added, "did I capture you?"

"Sire, truly," answered the count.

"Shake hands on it," said Aucassin.

"Willingly, Sire." He put his right hand in Aucassin's right hand.

"Now swear to me," Aucassin said, "that on no day of your life yet remaining for you to live you will ever shame my father or disturb him in either body or possessions, and that you swear you will not do it!"

"Sire, in God's name," he said, "quit jabbering at me and put me up for ransom. You will hardly name an amount in gold or in silver, in horses and palfreys, in ermine or in astrakhan, in dogs or in birds but I will owe it you."

"What's this?" asked Aucassin. "Do you not recognize the fact that I took you as my prisoner?"

"Sire, yes, I do," said Count Bougars.

"So help me God," said Aucassin," If you don't recognize it, but I'll send your head flying."

"God's name!" he said. "I do recognize it where and

227

whenever it pleases you." Then he made a solemn oath to that effect after which Aucassin allowed him to mount a horse. Aucassin mounted another and escorted him for a sufficient distance, or until Count Bougars was on safe ground.

. . . When Count Garins saw that he could not dissever his son Aucassin from Nicolette of the fair face, he put him in prison in a subterranean cell which was made of gray marble. After Aucassin had gone there, he was as sad as ever anyone was. He began to torment himself and to speak, as you shall hear:

"Nicolette, fleur-de-lis, sweet maiden of the fair face, sweeter yet than grapes or their juice in my maple cup. . . .

"The other yesterday I saw a pilgrim who was born in Limousin and was ill with vertigo.

"Thus he lay stretched upon his bed. His illness put him to great suffering; he was very sick of this great sickness. You passed beside his bed, and as you passed you raised the train of your gown, and you raised the ermine band of your cloak, and you raised your chemise of white linen . . . so much that he saw your limbs.

"The pilgrim was cured. He was all better, healthier than he ever was! He jumped up from his bed. Then he went home to his own land, hale and hearty and all completely cured.

"Sweetheart, fleur-de-lis, sweet comings and sweet goings, sweet games and sweet meetings, sweet speech and sweet delights, sweet kisses and sweet touchings. No man could ever hate you.

"For your sake was I put here in prison, here in this underground cell where I make much ado about much. Now it will suit me to die for you, dear one."

Or m'i couvenra morir
Por vos, amie.

—Just as you have heard and understood, Aucassin was put into prison while Nicolette was apart in her chamber. It was during the summertime in the month of May when the days are warm and long and sunny and the nights are calm and serene. As Nicolette lay one night on her bed, she saw the moon shining in clear at her window, and she heard the nightingales singing in the garden, and she lay remembering her lover Aucassin whom she loved so. Then she began to think about Count Garins de Biaucaire who hated her to the death. She thought to herself that she wouldn't remain there any longer, and that if she were formally indicted with Count Garin's knowledge, he would see to it that she died in agony.

She sensed that the old woman who was shut in with her was asleep. Nicolette got out of bed, dressed herself in a shift of a very good stuff which she had with her. Then she took her bed linen and her towels and tied them all together, piece to piece, until she had made a rope as long as possible. Then she knotted one end around one of the columns in the window. Then she climbed out and let herself down the sloping wall into the garden. Once on the ground she picked up her clothing, holding the front folds of her gown in one hand and the back folds in the other. Thus lifting it up because of the heavy dew she saw on the grass, she crossed the garden.

Her blond hair curled in little ringlets on her head. Her eyes were blue-green and laughing. He face was open like herself. Her nose was high-bridged and well-proportioned. Her little lips were crimson, redder than a cherry or a red rose in summertime, and her teeth were white and tiny. She had very firm little breasts which rose through her garments as if they were two ripe walnuts, and she was so slender in the hips that you could have held her there encircled in your two hands. And the daisy flowers that she crushed with the toes of her feet and which were bent until they lay under the arch of her instep appeared absolutely black compared to her feet and her limbs—so white was the little miss.

She made her way to the postern gate and unbarred it and stepped out into the streets of Biaucaire where they lay in shadow, for the moon was shining bright. She wandered so long that she finally came to the tower where her love was. Here and there the tower was buttressed. She flattened herself alongside one of these columns, tightly wrapped in her cloak, until she could find a fissure in the stone of the tower, which' was old and crumbling, through which she could put her head. She listened. Thus she heard Aucassin, who was sobbing inside and making a great to-do and lamenting his sweetheart whom he loved so. After she had listened for some time, she began to sing:

. . . "Nicolette of the fair face leaned against a column and heard Aucassin weeping. He was lamenting his sweetheart. Then she spoke. Then she told her thoughts.

"Aucassin, gentle and strong, frank and honored young lord, what good does it do you to rave, or complain, or shed tears when you can never be satisfied with loving me? You know your father hates me and so do just about all your relatives. For your sake I will cross over the sea. For you I will seek other kingdoms."

Then Nicolette cut off some locks of her hair and threw them inside to him. Gallant Aucassin took them and did them homage. He kissed her curls and caressed them. Then he slipped them close to his heart and began to weep again, all because of his sweetheart.

—When Aucassin heard Nicolette say that she intended to go to a foreign land, there was only wrath in him. "Beautiful sweetheart," he said, "you will not go away, for that would be the death of you. For the first man who saw you would immediately take you, if he could, and put you right in his bed and take care of you all right. And after you had

230

lain in a man's bed, unless it were mine, be sure I could hardly wait to find a knife so that I could drive it through my heart and kill myself.

"Don't think to see it, for I wouldn't wait that long! Either that, or I would hurl myself from as far as I could see a stone hut or a gray rock, and I would dash my head against it so hard I'd hurtle my eyes from their sockets, and so hard I'd knock out all my brains. Even so, I'd rather die such a horrible death than know that you had slept in a man's bed, unless it were mine."

"Oh me," she said. "I can't believe that you love me as much as you say, but I love you much more than you do me."

"Oh stop, sweetheart!" said Aucassin, "it just couldn't be that you love me more than I do you. No woman can love a man as much as a man loves a woman. A woman's love is in her clitoris, in the nipple of her breast, and in the tip of her big toe; but a man's love is planted deep in his heart from which it cannot issue."

As Aucassin and Nicolette were talking, the night watchmen of the city came marching down the street. Under their capes they held drawn swords, for Count Garins had ordered them to kill the girl if they could take her. The sentry who stood guard on the tower saw them coming. He heard them talking about Nicolette and threatening to slaughter her.

"God!" he said. "How terrible it would be if they killed the little miss. And there would be a great reward in it for me if I could tell them in some way so that they realized their danger and she took care of herself. For if they kill her, then my master Aucassin will die from it. That would be too dreadful."

. . . The sentry was a most valiant man, courageous and courtly and intelligent. Suddenly he began to sing a pretty, catchy little song:

"Mistress of the trusting heart, you have a soft and ap-

231

pealing body, blond and appealing curls, green eyes that
twinkle. I see very clearly from their sparkle that you have
been speaking to your love who is about to die from love of
you. Now I speak to you and hope you understand: Look
out for the soldiers. They're hunting for you. Under their
capes their swords are unsheathed. They're telling what
they will do to you. They will bring you to grief if you're
not on your guard."

—"Oh, you up there," cried Nicolette. "May the souls of
your father and your mother be at heavenly rest since you
have spoken so beautifully and so courteously to me! If God
pleases, I shall be on my guard, and may God guard me
from them!"

She blotted herself inside her cloak close to the shadow of
the buttress until they had passed by her and gone. Then she
bade farewell to Aucassin and walked away until she came
to the outer rampart of the castle. The ramparts had been
broken and had been carelessly piled stone upon stone again.
She was able to climb up to their summit until she could
see that she was standing between the curtain wall and the
moat. When she looked down and saw how steep the slope
was and how deep down the moat was, she became terribly
frightened.

"Ah, God! sweet creature!" she cried to herself, "If I let
myself drop, I will break my neck. On the other hand, if I
remain here, they will seize me tomorrow and burn me in
their fire. Even so, I would prefer to die right here than to
have all those people look at me tomorrow—as much as
they wanted."

She first made the sign of the cross and then let herself slide down the slope into the moat. When she had come
to the bottom, her pretty feet and hands, which had never
learned that they could be injured, were burned and
scratched, so much so that blood spurted out of them in
twelve places, despite which she felt neither pain nor hurt

for the great fear she had. And even as she had been in great difficulties to get down to the bottom, just so was she in a greater quandary as to how she could force her way up out again. She realized that it would be disastrous for her to stay where she was. Finally she found a sharpened stake which those inside had thrown down as they defended the castle. Using this, she dug footholds one above the other and climbed up, although with great pain, until she found herself on the outer rim.

There around the distance of two crossbow shots away was the forest, which stretched thirty leagues in depth and breadth, and in it were wild animals and snakes. She was afraid that if she entered it they would kill her. Then, on second thought, she realized that if they from the city found her there, they would take her back with them to be burned.

. . . Nicolette of the fair face climbed up from the moat. She began to lament and to call upon Jesus. "Our Father, King of Majesty, I don't know where to go now. If I go under the tall branches, the wolves will eat me or the lions or the wild boars, of which there are plenty. If I wait for the bright daylight and if they can find me here, the fire with which my body will be burned will be lighted. But still, God of Majesty, still I would rather enough be eaten by wolves and lions and boars than go back into that city. . . . I will not return."

—Nicolette cried out loud from fear, just as you have heard. Entrusting herself to God, she walked forward so long that she finally came to the forest. She did not dare plunge into the deep woods because of fierce animals and snakes; instead she crouched down under a thick bush where sleep overtook her. She slept until the following morning when at six o'clock the shepherds passed out of the city to pasture their beasts between the wood and the river. They themselves sat down by a very pretty spring which

233

was at the fringe of the forest. Then they spread out a cloak between them on which they laid their bread. As they sat there together eating, Nicolette was awakened by the songs of the birds and by the shepherds' voices. She hurried over to them.

"Good boys," she said, "May the Mother of God be with you."

"God bless you," said one who was a better talker than the others.

"Good boy," she said, "do you know Aucassin, son of Count Garins de Biaucaire?"

"Yes, we know him well."

"God keep you, good boy," she said. "Tell him that there is an animal in this forest and for him to come hunt it, and if he can capture it, he wouldn't give one of its limbs for a hundred golden marks, nor for five hundred, nor for any price."

The shepherds sat looking at her. They saw that she was beautiful—so beautiful that they were stunned.

"I shall tell him that?" said the one lad who was a better talker than the others. "May the person who will ever tell him that be ashamed of himself! You are talking about phantoms, and that's what! Why, there isn't any such beast in this forest at all—no deer nor lion nor wild boar one of whose limbs is worth more than two coins, or maybe three at the most. And you talk about such a great fortune! Ashamed be he who believes you, and I will never tell him any such thing! You are a fairy, and we don't care to associate with you at all, so be off on your way!"

"Oh, good boy," she said, "yes, you will tell him. This animal possesses such medicine that it will cure Aucassin of his wound. And I have five pennies in my purse. Here. Take them and tell it to him. And he ought to go hunting within three days, and if he does not find it within the three days, then he will never be cured of his wound."

234

"In faith," he said, "we will take your pennies, and if he comes this way, we will tell it to him; but we won't go out searching for him."

"God be with you," she said. Then Nicolette parted from the shepherds and went on her way.

. . . Nicolette of the fair face departed from the shepherds. She found a path under the leafy boughs. It was an old path, long frequented. She walked along until she came to a fork where the path became seven roads that stretched out in all directions over the country. All the time she was engrossed in trying to decide how she could test her love to see if he loved her as he said he did. As she pondered, she picked fleur-de-lis blossoms and grasses from under the scrub oak trees and leaves from here and there. With these she made as pretty a bower as ever anyone saw. Then she swore to God who does not lie that if Aucassin came by that way and if for love of her he did not stop to rest a bit in her bower that he would never again be her love nor she his.

—Nicolette had made her bower just as pretty and nice as you have heard and understood. She had simply filled it inside and out with flowers and leaves. Afterwards she made herself comfortable not far from her bower, in a thick clump of bushes. She hid there so she could see what Aucassin would do.

Meanwhile the news and the story that Nicolette had been lost spread over all the land and all the countryside. Some had it that she had fled; others reported that Count Garins had had her put to death. Whoever was glad of such a thing, Aucassin was not of their number. However, Count Garins his father had the youngster released from prison. He sent out summons and invitations to the knights and young gentry of his estates asking them to attend a very sumptuous festival. He thought that by doing this he could comfort his son.

At the very moment when the party was the loudest,

Aucassin himself was leaning on the rim of a well. He was bent with pain. Whoever else might be having a gay time, Aucassin had no taste for merriment when he saw not a single person or single thing he loved anywhere near him. A certain knight who noticed him standing there said to Aucassin, "I, too, was once afflicted by the same illness that ails you, Aucassin, and just as severely. I will offer you some good advice, if you care to give any credit to what I say."

"Sire," replied Aucassin, "my sincere thanks. I should consider such advice valuable."

"Get on your horse then," he said. "Take a ride out into the forest for the fun of it. You will see the flowers and the grasses there. You will hear the little birds sing. Maybe you will even hear such words as will make you feel better."

"Sire," said Aucassin, "my sincere thanks to you. I will do it."

He hurried from the hall, ran down the staircase, and went to the stables where the horses were. He had saddle and bridle put on his horse. He put his left foot in the stirrup and swung into the saddle. He rode forth from the castle and on until he came to the forest and kept going until he came to the fountain where he found the shepherds. It was then about three o'clock in the afternoon. Their cloak was still spread on the grass. They were eating their bread and having a wonderful time.

. . . The shepherd lads were gathered there: Emery and little Martin, Freulins and Johnnie, Robin boy and little Aubrey. One of them said, "God be with little old Aucassin, dear friend."

"Hear! Hear! On my word, the handsome lad . . . and also the little Miss Muffet whose hair is so blondette, whose face is so fair, and whose eyes are such bluets, who gave us her pennies so we could buy goodies, and jackknives in holders, reed flutes and bagpipes, cudgels and fifes. . . . God save her!"

—As soon as Aucassin heard the shepherd lads, he immediately connected their songs with his sweetheart Nicolette, whom he loved so. Right away he believed that she had been there. He dug his spurs into his horse's sides and rode up close to them.

"Good fellows, God keep you!"

"God bless you," said the one who spoke better than the others.

"Good lad," he said, "would you sing that song again—the one you were just singing?"

"No, we will not sing it again," replied the one who spoke better than the others. "Anyone who sang it before you, fine Sir, would be embarrassed."

"Good boy," said Aucassin, "don't you recognize me?"

"Yes, we know all right that you are our young lord Aucassin, but we are not your men. We belong to the count."

"Good lad, you will sing for me, I beg you."

"Hear him, on my blessed heart!" he said. "Why should I sing for you unless it happened to suit me? Why, there isn't a man in this country so rich—exception made always for Count Garins—who if he found my cows and my oxen and my sheep in his meadows or in his wheat fields, whether or not he were daring enough to have my eyes put out, at least he would dare have my herds driven away. . . . So why should I sing for you, unless it suits me?"

"God be with you, good lad. You will do it. And here are ten pennies which I happen to have in my purse."

"Sire, we will take your money, but I will absolutely not sing for you because I made an oath not to. However, I will recite the words for you, if you like."

"For God's sake, do so," said Aucassin. "I'd rather have you tell me the words than nothing."

"Sire, we were here just a while ago, between six and nine o'clock; we were eating our bread for breakfast just as we are now here by this spring when a maiden came past, the prettiest little thing in the world, so much so that at first we thought she was a fairy and that all the woods lighted up where she went. However, she gave us such and such moneys for us to make a bargain with her that, if you came along by here, we would tell you that you should go hunting in this forest, that there is an animal here of which, if you could take it, you would not exchange one of the limbs for five silver marks, nor for any amount; for this beast possesses such medicine that if you could take it you would be cured of your malady; and also that it must be your agreement to have taken it within three days, and if at the end of that time you have not taken it, you will never see it again. So hunt for it if you wish; and if you so wish, let it go. For I have now acquitted myself as far as she is concerned."

"Good boy," said Aucassin, "you have said enough about it, and God grant me to find it."

. . . Aucassin heard the words of his sweetheart of the lovely body. They sank deep into his own being. He soon left the shepherds and plunged into the deep woods. His war horse went at a good clip. He covered ground fast at a gallop. As he rode, he had three words to say to himself:

"It is for you, Nicolette of the lovely body, that I have come to these woods. I hunt neither deer nor wild pig but follow the spoor towards you. Your green eyes and your pretty body and your lovely laugh and your sweet words have pierced my heart to death [*"Ont men cuer navre a mort"*]. If God, the Powerful Father, pleases, I shall see you again, oh my sister, my sweetheart."

—Aucassin rode from one forest trail into another, his horse carrying him all this time at top speed. Don't suppose that briars and thorns spared him at all! Not a bit of it at all! They so badly ripped his garments that one could not have found an untorn piece to sew over the holes, so ripped at him that blood ran down his arms and his sides and his legs in forty places or in thirty, and so freely that one could have followed the youngster's trail by the blood which fell on the grass. However, he was thinking so hard of his sweetheart Nicolette that he felt neither wounds nor pain. He rode all day through the forest as fast as he could, but still found no further trace of her.

Now when Aucassin realized that the time of vespers was drawing near, tears began to form in his eyes, for he had not found her. Just before dusk he turned down an old grass-grown path. As he peered down the trail ahead of him, he saw a young man such as I will tell you. He was tall and marvelous to see and ugly and hideous. He had a big animal's head blacker than a lump of coal. His eyes were as wide apart as the breadth of a good-sized palm. He had fat cheeks and the biggest flat nose and big, wide nostrils and thick lips redder than meat cooked over a grill, and a few ugly, yellow teeth. He was wearing leggings and high shoes of rawhide that were laced with bast all the way above the knee. He was wrapped about with a cloak that had two linings and leaning upon a massive club. . . . Aucassin bore down upon him; but as he looked closer, he was afraid.

"Good brother, God save you."

"God bless you," said he.

"As God keeps you, what are you doing here?"

"That's your business?" said he.

"Not at all," said Aucassin. "I wouldn't ask if not for a good reason."

"But what are you weeping about?" he asked. "Why are you mourning so loudly? For sure, if I were such an important man as you are, the whole world couldn't make me weep."

"Bah! Do you recognize me?" asked Aucassin.

"Yes. I know you are Aucassin, the count's son. If you tell me why you are weeping, I'll tell you what I am doing here."

"Certainly," said Aucassin, "I will tell you most gladly. This morning I came here to the forest to hunt. I had with me a pure, white greyhound, the most beautiful in the century. I lost it. That's why I weep."

"Oof!" he said, "for the kind of heart such a lord has in his belly! That you should weep for a stinking dog! Shame on him who will ever respect you, when there is not another rich man in this country who if your father commanded ten or fifteen or twenty greyhounds from him would not give them to you and who would not be very happy to do so. As for me, I have a right to weep and make mourning."

"You, brother? For what?"

"Sire, I will tell you. I was hired out to a rich serf, and so I did his ploughing. He had four oxen. Well, three days ago the worst misfortune happened to me. I lost Roget, the best of my team, the best of my oxen, and so I go about hunting for him. Also I have neither eaten nor drunk a drop for the three past days, and I don't dare go into town for fear they would put me in jail. And I have nothing at all with which to pay the damages. As my entire wealth in this world all I have that is of value is what you see on my body. I had a weary old mother. All she owned of any value was a small quilt, and so they dragged that out from under her body. Now she lies on the bare straw. That hurts me more than for myself.

"Possessions come and go. If I lose my money, I'll earn some more. I'll pay for the ox, too, when I can. And it's not for a thing like that that I will cry. But you actually shed tears for a dog of the backhouse! Shame upon him who will ever respect you!"

"Truly, you are a real comfort to me, good brother, and may you be blessed. What was the worth of your ox?"

"Sire, they want twenty pennies for him. I can't beat them down by a single hair."

"Well, here," said Aucassin, "are twenty that I have with me in my purse. So go pay for your ox."

"Sire," he said, "thank you very much. And may God let you find what you are seeking." Then he took leave of him.

Aucassin rode ahead. The night was fair and still, and he wandered so long that he finally came to the fork where the seven roads branched out before him. As he peered ahead, he saw the pretty lodge that Nicolette had made. It was stuffed outside and inside and over its roof with flowers. It was as pretty as pretty could be. As soon as Aucassin saw it, he halted immediately. A ray of moonlight shone inside the bower.

"My God," said Aucassin, "my sweetheart Nicolette was here. She made this with her beautiful hands. On account of her sweetness and for love of her, I will dismount here and rest myself overnight."

He took his feet out of the stirrups to dismount. His horse was tall and high. He was so engrossed in thoughts of his sweetheart Nicolette that he fell heavily. He struck his shoulder such a blow on a rock that it slipped from its socket. He realized that he was badly hurt. However, he persevered so hard that he managed with his good hand to tie his horse to a thorn bush. Then he rolled over on his side so that he ended up lying on his back in the bower. From where he lay he could see the stars in the sky. One of them was brighter than the others. Then he began to speak.

. . . "I see you, little star which the moon is drawing towards her. Nicolette, my little love with the blond curls, is beside you. I believe that God wants to elect her to be the light of evening. . . .* However great my falling down would be, I wish I were up in the heavens with thee! I would kiss thee so closely, if I were a king's son, and you could be confident of my troth."

---

* Three lines are missing from the manuscript here.

241

—When Nicolette heard Aucassin's voice, she went to him. She had not been far away. She entered the bower, threw her arms about his neck, and kissed him, and hugged him.

"Beautiful sweetheart, how glad I am you are found again."

"And you, beautiful sweetheart, how glad I am you are found." Then they kissed and hugged each other again and again. Their joy was wonderful. "Ah, sweetheart," said Aucassin, "a few minutes ago I hurt my shoulder, but now that I have you again, I feel neither pain nor hurting!"

She palpated his shoulder and found that it was out of the socket. She so handled it with her two white hands and so pulled it—and this is how God wills lovers to love—that it snapped back into place again. Then she gathered flowers, fresh herbs, and certain leaves which she bound to it with a bandage made from her chemise. Aucassin was then completely healed.

"Aucassin," she said, "beautiful sweetheart, take counsel as to what you will do. If tomorrow your father had a search made through this forest and if they find me, whatever may happen to you, they will kill me."

"Certainly, beautiful love, I would be most grief-stricken if such a thing happened. But if I can help it, they won't capture you." He mounted his horse and lifted his love up before him. Then kissing and hugging each other, they rode away singing:

. . . "Aucassin the handsome, the blond, the gentle and so much in love, rode away through the deep forest with his loved one in his arms, with his loved one on the pommel before him. He kissed her eyes, and he kissed her forehead, and her lips, and her chin."

Then she spoke sensibly to him: "Aucassin, beautiful love, into what land shall we go?"

"Sweetheart, how do I know? Little I care where we go—

into a forest or into an uninhabited land—so long as I may be with you!"

They traveled through valleys and over mountains and into cities and towns. One day they came to the sea. They dismounted on the sandy beach of the seashore.

—Aucassin dismounted between the sea and his love, just as you have heard and understood. He held the reins with one hand and his love by the other. Thus they began to walk along the shore. . . .*

He hailed them and they rowed in towards him. He arranged for them to take passage on the vessel. When they were far out to sea, a marvelously great storm arose which swept them from one land to another until they finally were able to go ashore in a foreign land. They had entered the harbor which belonged to the castle of Torelore. Once disembarked, they inquired as to what land it was. They were told that the land belonged to the King of Torelore. They then asked what sort of man he was and whether or not he was at war.

"Yes, greatly," they were told.

Aucassin bade farewell to the merchants, who commended him to God. He mounted his horse again, buckled on his sword, took his love up beside him, and rode on until he came to the castle. There he asked where the king was. He was informed that the king was in labor.

"And where is his wife?"

They told him that she was with the army where she had led all the people from that country. When Aucassin heard all this, he was very much amazed. He rode up to the palace and dismounted between it and his beloved. While she held the horse's bridle, he climbed the steps to the palace. He kept his sword in its scabbard. He wandered

* There is a *lapsus* in the manuscript here.

243

about until he came to the room where the king lay in bed.

, . . Aucassin entered the chamber. He was courtly and noble. He went across the room and up to the bed upon which the king lay. He halted in front of it and said, "Oh! What are you doing here?"

Said the king, "I'm giving birth to a son. When my months are up, I will be delivered all right and churched so I can hear mass just as my ancestors before me have done. And I shall not abandon the mighty war I am fomenting against my enemies."

When Aucassin heard the king talk like that, he grabbed all the covers and sheets which were over him and tumbled them in a heap across the room. He saw a stick behind him. He took it, raised it, brought it down, and beat the king so hard he almost killed him.

"Ha! fine sir," said the king, "what do you want from me? Have your wits been addled that you beat me in my own house?"

"By God's heart," said Aucassin, "dirty son of a whore, I will kill you if you don't swear to me that no man in your country will ever again give birth to a child."

The king so swore. When he had made his oath, Aucassin ordered, "Sire, now take me to where your wife is with the army."

"Sire, willingly," said the king.

He mounted his horse and Aucassin mounted his, leaving Nicolette in the queen's chamber. The king and Aucassin rode along until they came to the place where the queen was. There they found a battle raging with baked crabapples, with eggs, and with fresh cheeses. As Aucassin began to look around him, he was most appallingly amazed.

. . . Aucassin remained leaning forward over the pommel of his saddle as he began to stare at this full-scale field engagement. They had brought as their weapons plenty of freshly made cheeses and lots of baked crabapples and some great big meadow mushrooms. He who best roils up the fords is acclaimed the best man.

The gallant and baronly Aucassin stared at them. Then he began to laugh.

—When Aucassin saw this wonder, he went up to the king and asked him, "Sire, are these people here your enemies?"

"Yes, Sire," replied the king.

"Would you like me to take revenge upon them for you?"

"Yes," he said, "I would."

Then Aucassin put his hand to his sword and charged the foe. He began to swing right and left in order to kill a great many of them. When the king saw that he was actually killing them, he halted Aucassin by taking hold of his bridle. "Oh, fine Sir," he said, "don't kill them so completely!"

"Why not?" asked Aucassin. "Don't you want me to get revenge for you?"

"Sire," said the king, "you have already done too much. It is not our custom at all to kill each other."

Meanwhile the others had fled far away. Therefore the king and Aucassin returned to the castle of Torelore. There the people of that land told the king to throw Aucassin out of the country and to detain Nicolette as a bride for his son since she seemed to be a lady of such noble lineage.

When Nicolette heard this, she was so far from happy! She sang this song:

. . . "Sir King of Torelore, hear what pretty Nicolette has to say. Your subjects think I am foolish when my sweetheart embraces me. I feel plump and soft to him, and this is the kind of schooling I enjoy. Neither balls, nor country dances, nor caroling, nor harp, nor viols, nor fiddles, nor the delights of the Maypole can compare with his lovemaking."

—Aucassin was thus in the castle of Torelore with his beloved Nicolette. There he was relaxed and superbly happy, for he had with him his sweetheart Nicolette whom he loved so. While they were amusing themselves and enjoying life, a fleet of Saracen ships arrived by sea to storm the castle. They took it after a short battle. They looted its goods and took both men and women prisoners. They captured both Aucassin and Nicolette.

They tied Aucassin hand and foot and threw him into one of their ships. They put Nicolette into another vessel. After they had put out to sea, a storm separated the two ships. The vessel where Aucassin was imprisoned went wallowing over the sea so long that it finally went aground near the castle of Biaucaire. When the people of that land ran out to plunder the wreck, they found the prisoner whom they recognized as Aucassin. They were most joyful to see him. During the three years which he had spent in the castle of Torelore, his father and mother had died. The people escorted Aucassin to his castle of Biaucaire where they swore fealty to him. Aucassin ruled his country in peace.

. . . Aucassin thus went away to his own land of Biaucaire where he became rightful ruler of both land and city. He swore to Almighty God that he grieved more for Nicolette of the fair face than for all members of his own family who had gone to their appointed ends.

"Sweetheart of the fair face, I do not know where to quest for you. God, however, never created a kingdom over lands or over the seas where I would not go questing for you if I thought I could find you."

—Now let us leave aside Aucassin and tell of what happened to Nicolette. The ship where she was belonged to the king of Carthage, and he was her father. Nicolette had twelve brothers, all of them princes or kings. When they saw Nicolette so beautiful, they paid her the highest honors. They made much ado about her. They kept asking her who she was, for she seemed to them to be a gentlewoman of very noble lineage. However, she could not tell them a single word about herself, for she had been lost when she was a very small child.

Her ship rowed along so well that finally it arrived in the port of Carthage. When Nicolette saw the walls of the citadel and the country itself, she suddenly realized that she had been born there and raised there. She remembered having been taken from there as a young child—not so young, however, that she did not know who she was. She then recalled perfectly well that she was daughter to the king of Carthage and that she had been raised right there in that city.

. . . The gallant and wise Nicolette arrived upon the shores of Carthage, saw its walls and buildings, its palaces and its halls. Appalled, she cried to herself, "What a sad thing for me that I come of royal blood, that I was born daughter to the king of Carthage and cousin of its admiral! This is where these wild sailors are taking me!

"Gentle and wise Aucassin, honorable and honest nobleman, your love binds me to you and summons me and makes me eager for you. May Merciful God grant me to be held once more in your arms, kissed once more by your lips on my lips and on my face, oh, Sir Lord!"

—When the king of Carthage heard her words, he threw his arms about her shoulders and said, "Beautiful, sweet girl, tell me who you are. Do not be timid in front of me."

"Sire," she said, "I am the daughter to the king of Carthage. I was captured here as a young child, about fifteen years ago."

As soon as he heard her speak in this way, he knew that she was telling the truth. Therefore he gave her a royal welcome, leading her into the palace as became the daughter of a king. His barons wanted to give her one of the pagan kings, but she had no desire to be married. She remained there for three days, or four. During this time she wracked her brains as to what scheme she could find in order to search for Aucassin.

Nicolette requested a viol. Then she learned to play. When the time came that they finished their plans for her to wed a rich pagan king, she slipped out of the palace one night. She went down to the sea. There she found temporary refuge with a poor, old woman who lived right on the shore. She took a certain herb with which she made an ointment for her head and her face. She dyed her hair and skin until she was completely black. Then she had made for herself a short coat and a cloak, a shirt and trousers. When she had dressed in these garments, she looked exactly like a minstrel.

Then Nicolette took her viol and went hunting for a ship's master. She bargained with one until he agreed to take her aboard his ship. Sails were hoisted. The ship cleared the port and sped over the water so swiftly that they soon came to shore at the land of Provence. Nicolette disembarked along with her viol. From there she traveled singing and playing from place to place throughout that country until she finally arrived at the castle of Biaucaire where Aucassin was.

. . . One day Aucassin was sitting on the staircase leading down from the tower of Biaucaire. His lords were around him. As he looked at the grass and the flowers, as he heard the little birds singing, he was thinking of gallant Nicolette, whom he had loved so many days. Then he sighed and wept as he remembered her. All of a sudden Nicolette herself appeared on the marble staircase. She lifted her viol and her bow. Then she began to tell a story:

"Listen to me, fine lords, those above and below! Would you care to hear a song about a very great lord named Aucassin and his gallant Nicolette? Their loves lasted so long that he searched for her in a dark forest. One day heathen pirates captured them in the tower of Torelore.

We know nothing of Aucassin's fate. Nicolette, however, is in the donjon at Carthage; for her father, the ruler of that kingdom, loves her dearly. The lords of that land wish to give her a king of the wretched pagans. Nicolette has no desire for such a husband, for she loves a young nobleman whose name is Aucassin. She has taken an oath to God and in His name that she will never have any other master than her love whom she desires so."

—When Aucassin heard Nicolette speak this way, he was all overjoyed. He took the minstrel aside to ask, "Fine and gentle friend, do you know anything at all about the Nicolette in your song?"

"Yes, Sire. I know that she is the most honest creature and the nicest and the best-behaved girl who was ever born. She certainly is the daughter of the king of Carthage who took her prisoner in the same place where Aucassin was captured. They took her to the city of Carthage. When he found out that she was his daughter, the king rejoiced to see her again. Every day he wants her to be married to one of the highest kings of all Spain, but she would sooner let herself be hanged or burned at the stake than marry any one of them, no matter how important he was."

"Oh, good friend," said Aucassin, "if you were to return to that land, if you were to tell her to come speak to me, I would give you so much of my wealth as you would never dare ask for or accept. And know that for love of her I do not wish to take a wife, no matter how high her birth, but I wait for her and will never have another wife but her. And if I had known where to find her I would have sought her long since."

"Sire," she said, "if you would do this, then I would go to seek her, for your sake and for hers whom I love dearly."

He swore it and then had given to the minstrel twenty pounds. When the singer was about to leave, Aucassin shed tears because of Nicolette's sweetness.

"Sire," said the minstrel, "do not be dismayed. Within a very short time I shall bring her into this city so that you will see her before you."

When Aucassin heard this, he was delighted. The minstrel departed towards the house of the viscountess, for the viscount, Nicolette's godfather, had died. She took lodging there and told the viscountess so much of her adventures that she was recognized and welcomed as the Nicolette whom that lady had raised. Her godmother had her washed and bathed. For eight full days Nicolette remained in her old home. She took a certain weed called celandine from which she made an ointment that bleached her skin. Then she became more beautiful than she ever on any day before had been.

Nicolette dressed in a gown of rich silken stuff, for the lady had a great choice of precious fabrics. Then she seated herself in a chamber upon quilted cushions of heavy silk. She summoned her godmother and asked her to send for her friend Aucassin. The lady went herself. When she entered the palace, she found Aucassin weeping and sorrowful for his love Nicolette about whom he had been so many days without news.

The lady greeted him and said, "Do not grieve any longer, Aucassin. Instead, come away with me. I shall show you what you most love in the world. I will show you your sweetheart Nicolette who has come searching for you from such faraway lands."

And Aucassin was glad.

. . . When Aucassin heard that his beloved of the fair face had returned to his country, he was glad, gladder than he ever before had been. He accompanied the viscountess. They did not pause until they had entered her hall. They did not stop until they had entered the chamber where Nicolette sat.

When she saw her love, then she was happy. She never was so happy. She ran into his arms.

As soon as Aucassin saw her, he stretched out both his arms. He folded them gently all about her. He kissed her eyes and her face. All night they stayed that way until the next morning when Aucassin married her. He made her Lady of Biaucaire.

They lived happily many a day after that. Aucassin enjoyed his love and so did Nicolette.

No cantefable prent fin
N'en sai plus dire.

Our musical comedy ends here. I know no more.

XI

THE LAY OF A SHADOW

Jehan Renart

THIRTEENTH CENTURY

I CANNOT let my skill in words fall into disuse. Instead, let me use my skill rather than disabuse it in idleness. I have no desire to resemble those who are good at destruction: since I have a taste for construction and can create something worthy in either language or plot, I shall consider those who ridicule me as low fellows. Only my sense of what courtesy is urges me to write a pleasant work where there is neither spite nor ugliness. And even if some critic were to use his language backwards and forwards, which is as it may be, no more than I could make this finger longer than that one, no more could he turn a scoundrel like himself into a good man. . . . It is better to have been born under a lucky star than to have such men as friends, and I've said that before.

253

According to William's example—you remember how in the story he cut the kite* into pieces and burned them— you can be sure I am telling you a truth when I say that a man is better off to have been born with talent even than to have friends. A friend dies and one is too often powerless to keep a friend if one does not watch out or if he falls under the influence of a fool. But a person who wastes his words and squanders his riches and afterwards accuses Folly because he spent extravagantly, if when the move has been made, if he puts aside the follies he has committed, and if his bad luck runs out, then his lucky star will twinkle on him again.

This is why I made my present decision. I wish to use my skill in words in telling you a good story and in modulating it to the loftiness of my material. Great, indeed, is my delight as an author when my hard work has succeeded in creating a thing of beauty, such as a romance put into rhyme.

Someone has said: He who rows well and rhymes well, he who pulls safely to shore from the deep ocean, he who arrives fairly at the port of literature . . . is more to be esteemed than kings and counts. . . . So in due time you shall hear this story I will tell you, if boredom does not meanwhile descend upon us both, this lay I shall make of a shadow.

I tell you there was once a knight from the outer marches

* The author is presumably referring to a romance called *L'Escoufle* named rather charmingly from the kite bird or hawk which caused William to be separated from his love during their elopement; our author of this *Lay of a Shadow* is probably also the author of *L'Escoufle*.

of the Empire of Lorraine and Germany. I don't suppose one such remains today from Châlons to Perthois who unites in his person such an array of fine qualities as he did. In many respects he resembled Sir Gawain, the son of Lot, as we know. However, we never heard his name. I don't even know if he had one. In any case, he did have prowess and courteousness as his proper domains. All who were acquainted with him marveled at the rich train of life he led. You would have found that he was neither too talkative nor too haughty, nor at all boorish. Although he wasn't a particularly wealthy man, he did know how to live handsomely with what he had. He knew how to take the surplus from one place to cover the scarcity of another. Neither lady nor damsel ever heard tell of him without liking what they heard and even bearing him a certain affection, but he took none of them seriously. It was not that he was not desired, for in every respect he was open and charming and gallant. When persons wanted his company, they were welcome and more than welcome as his guests.

However, when it came to contests of arms, then he was quite another man from the one I have been describing. Proud and defiant and daring whenever he wore a helmet on his head, he knew how to ride down the files of mounted and visored knights and challenge them to break a lance with him. He insisted upon two jousts every holy day. Among all other brave knights there was not one so devoted to armed contests as he was, nor was he a man to wear his summer finery in winter. With gifts and furs he was generous to a fault, bestowing lavishly more than any two other knights.

Every day he liked to have five or so friends about him, nor did he ever have a thing in his hands that someone else coveted without his immediately offering it to him. He also enjoyed hawking when he was in the mood. I don't dislike it, either. He knew how to play chess and how to skirmish and to play all sorts of other "games" better even than Tristran. For a long time he lived such a carefree life that he was beloved by many people. In body and motions he was handsome and light and quick. Perhaps he was actually more a valiant than a really pretty man. In short, he was everything a knight should be.

Then Love, which makes itself master or mistress of all she surveys, at this opportune moment in his life ran him through. Love wanted to exact tribute from him for all the pleasure he had so far lightly enjoyed in his life. Although he had delighted many a lady in his days, he had never bound himself in either service or homage and still did not do so since he never had recognized his state as a lover within Love's harsh bailiwick. Hence Love, in due time and due place, let him feel her might.

Even Tristran, who once cut off his hair and dressed as a jester for the sake of Yseut, never felt a third of the love-sickness this knight felt for her upon whom his recovery depended. Love shot an arrow into him, right through the body and up to the feathers. Then the great beauty and the lovely name of a certain married lady was engraved by Love in his heart. Then he naturally put far away all the other women he had known. His heart had been involved in many pastimes without doting upon any of them. From that moment he saw that he could put their various attractions all together in order to serve her who seemed to him to be the priceless ruby among all beauties.

The perceptiveness, the nobility, and the great gentleness of her glowing face was, to the best of my knowledge, before his eyes both day and night. There was no longer any joy that didn't bore him except only the joy alone of thinking of her. Love, who knew him well, had set such a perfect trap for him that he said he had never seen such a thing as lovely as this woman was, and he was ready to go bond for it.

257

"Ah!" he said, "I have thus far been so miserly with my love and so clever at avoiding danger! Now God wishes those who bestowed their love on me, those whom I did not love, to be avenged. I have certainly misjudged all those men whom I have seen surprised by Love. Now I have been reduced to the same condition. Love wants me to feel her power. There never was a poor devil sitting in the barber's chair to have his teeth pulled who felt more anguish than I do."

That is the sort of thing he thought and said when he was alone, for truly he was no longer his own master. No man before had ever been placed in a more cruel torment than that in which Love had set him.

"Alas!" he said. "Since I am in love with her, what will happen if she is never in love with me? That I don't know, nor do I see how I can live a day longer. Delight from going or from staying cannot relieve my heart nor bring solace. There is nothing else to do but to cultivate the friendship of those who ordinarily go where she is; by so doing many have had joy and relief for their love. If only she would make a chain with her two arms about my neck! All night long I imagine that she kisses me and that she is holding me and that her arms are close about me. Our awakening in the morning unkisses me from my delight. Then I hunt for her in my bed and feel for her beautiful body which sets me on fire and binds me to its spell." (But, alas, he who cannot find, cannot take. . . . It has happened to me and has happened many a time to many another man.)

"Well, it cannot be otherwise. I shall have to go to her or send her entreaties, since it cannot be otherwise. I shall ask her to take pity finally on my distress, ask that from her great gentleness she save my life and my mind. There would be one less of hers if she allowed me to perish. By all good right only kindness should flow from her heart, only pity from her eyes.

"Upon reflection, it occurs to me that it would be better for me to go to her than to send her messages. They say: 'There's nothing like action' that so becomes a man. They used to say in the old days that experience and suffering are two very good teachers. Since I have managed to appeal to my own reason, the only thing to do is to go directly to her and say frankly that she has imprisoned my heart which never before knew love and that it has no desire to escape, so sad is it. . . . Gentleness, pity, and generosity ought to be able to move her."

To move her, he outfitted himself and two of his companions—no more. I don't know what more I should tell you than that he mounted, with up to six valets. He cantered along, happy and pensive in his thoughts and on his way. He took care to mislead his companions as to the reason for his journey and to throw them off the track of his thoughts. He told them that he was just going for a gay ride. Thus he buried his anxiety under a carefree appearance so well that they all came without suspicion up to the porter's lodge at the entrance to her castle.

"See how pleasantly that castle is situated!" he remarked. He didn't say it so much for the moats and the walls to which he pointed but only to see if by some lucky chance his men would speak of the beautiful lady he was going to see.

"You ought to be ashamed," said they, "for you have acted badly in that you mentioned the castle first instead of first mentioning that lady who everyone says is the most courteous and the most beautiful in the realm.

"Oh, on guard," said they, "for if she knew what an error you have made, it would be better for you to have been captured by the Turks and taken to Cairo."

With a smile he said, "Oh, Sirs, in God's name, treat me kindly. Don't handle me so roughly. I haven't quite deserved to die. There's not a city nor a castle I more desire to see than this one. I'd go to Saladin's prison for five years or six if I were guaranteed that it would be mine, seated just as it is."

"And what about what's inside its walls?" they asked. "Would that be too much to the bargain?" All this time they didn't even understand what sophistry he was leading them into saying. The good knight was only talking to hear what they would say. He asked them if they wanted to call. "What else would we do?" they replied. "Knights ought never to pass by a road or a highway where a lady dwells without stopping to see her."

He said, "I shall abide by your wishes, and if you advise and wish that we go, then that is reason enough."

Then each pulled on his steed's reins and turned them towards the gateway, crying: "For the ladies, a party of knights!" (For such an enterprise, such a refrain.)

They spurred their horses dashingly up to the citadel. They had already passed the moat and the first wall. The lord had draped his cloak across one shoulder, with the collar against his cheek. He wore an ermined surcoat made of very shiny scarlet silk with bands of squirrel. As for the others, they wore pleated white shirts, hats trimmed with periwinkle blossoms and spurs of burnished gold. I can't imagine how any one could be more pleasingly clad for a summer's day. . . .

They didn't pull up their horses until they had clattered up to the staircase of honor that led to the great hall. Every valet in the castle had heard the commotion and run to the balconies. The seneschal of the household saw the knights dismounting in the courtyard. From the office where he was, he ran to tell the lady the news—that certain knights, whom she knew only by hearsay, had come to pay her a visit.

The lady became crimson, not with anger, but because this visit was so unexpected. She stood up on her crimson carpet, and there she stood full height, this lady of great beauty. Her maidens threw about her shoulders a mantle of white samite, which enhanced the great beauty which was hers by nature. She had intended to go down to greet the knights, but they were so quick to mount the staircase that they were already in the chamber before she could leave it. By the glad face she showed them, they knew they were welcome. The knights were delighted that she honored them by advancing even a few steps, instead of waiting for them to cross the room to her.

The courteous and high-born lady wore over her gown a loose and diaphanous white tunic with a train that floated six feet behind her on the fine rushes of the floor.

"Sir," she said to the knight, "you are very welcome and your companions also." She bore herself like a person who has every day a good-day on her lips and who is every bit worthy of having one. The companions had spoken the truth when they said she was no lady whose house should be by-passed. As they bowed low and returned her greeting, all three were under the spell of her beauty.

Laughing softly, the lady took the knight by the hand and led him to a seat. Then he had what he had so long desired, when he sat by her side. Fortunately, the knight's companions were well-mannered and sophisticated. Instead of making the conversation general, they sat, with two of the lady's attendants, on a large chest studded with brass. Because they were enchanted by their own damsels who chatted easily with them, the companion knights gave no thought to their master and hostess.

On her side of the chamber the lady, by the wit and grace of her words, taught the knight how very courteous and intelligent she really was. He leaned towards her so that his face was so close he could admire the beauty of her eyes. He called mutely upon her eyes to bear witness to his heart's predicament—since it was utterly hers—so that she could see that from the instant he had promised it to her, he had not done so falsely.

"Very lovely, very sweet, most beloved Lady," he said, "the power of your heart has cast and thrown far out of myself all thoughts other than thoughts of you. I come, therefore, before you today to lay at your feet my strength and my power inasmuch as I possess either. I come to learn if I shall ever have any joy; for truly there is no one and no thing I love so much as I love you. If the all-knowing God lets me come into His grace, to know this have I come here today, as I wish you to realize that you are the mistress of my person. And may gentleness and pity overcome your heart. For a man who would say prayers in a minster would do well to pray for those who understand nothing of love or who know not how to be a loyal love."

"Why, Sir, upon my soul," she said, "what have you said?"

"So God lets me live until Saint Denis's day, Lady, I have only said the truth. You and you alone have power over me, and that more than any woman alive."

The lady blushed flame-red to hear him confess his love, and even redder when he swore he was hers alone. After a while she said most sensibly, "Certainly, Sir, I cannot believe that such a chivalrous knight as yourself is without a true love, as you say. Nor would anyone else believe it either. Your stock would fall everywhere. You would be esteemed much lower than at present you are esteemed. Such a handsome man in every respect—in arms and hands and body and everything else—would certainly know by word and by glance how to pull the wool over my eyes and make me take for the truth what I don't want to take."

Thus right at the outset she succeeded by her words in casting serious doubt on his protestations, as he who taught me this story explained. He suffered at having been brought up short when he swore there was no one he loved so much. If any other but her had implied he was a liar, he would have taken a quick revenge; however, he was on such ticklish ground that he still did not dare contradict her.

Instead, he spoke sensibly: "Oh, Lady, have mercy on me. Take pity. Without feint, love of you made me discover for the first time the lovesickness I feel. Your speech and your lovely eyes hardly harmonize with what you say now. They greeted me more pleasantly a few minutes ago when I came—and more warmly. And know for sure that when they welcomed me, that was true courtesy. But when your eyes first caught sight of me, they saw nothing, and that's the long and the short of it, unless you wish to take me as your man, for that—without deceit—I desire to be. . . . Sweet Lady, out of your gentleness, may it please you to so ordain!

"Retain me as your knight as of now—and when you will, as your love. For the past year and a half you have put me under your spell, you have made me so true to arms or to my household, and you have charmed me so that the name of love, God willing, will never be refused me."

"It does you great good," she said afterwards, "for you to think you have this position. I meant nothing by my glances except courtesy and respect. But I must say it grieves me that you have interpreted them as light. If I had not welcomed you courteously, that would have been very dishonorable of me. It is a silly thing that we ladies are so unseeing. When we think we are fulfilling the obligations of chivalry and the requirements of good manners, men think entirely otherwise —that they have advanced their own suits.

"My experience with you today has done nothing if not prove it. You drew this same conclusion. You should have done better to hold up a net for pigeons, for, were the years as long as you say and the halves like three full ones, you would never know well enough how to wangle—not for anything you knew how to do—me into being as gallant in my behavior to you as you begged me to be. A man should be more cautious, before he sets his net, about what he is doing."

Then the knight could not see what, by word or by deed, he was going to do or to become. "At least, Lady," he began, "I cannot deny what I have been. There is pity and kindness in you, and never doubt it. They never failed us. A lady truly beloved never failed in the end to take pity on her lover. So I have put out to sea, like Tristran, without a mast. Just as I was for a long time master of my own ship and just as I steered my own course, if I do not receive your forgiveness today, I shall never consider any other failure a sorrow when I shall have escaped from this one. My heart, which set itself upon you without so much as your leave, can sue for no other redress."

"Oh, really," she said with a laugh, "I never heard anything like this! . . . Well, you may remain here a little longer. I am convinced that what you say is not entirely wind. And yet, by Saint Nicholas, I first thought you were joking."

"In God's name, even if you were the lowest little harlot, most honored and beautiful and gentle Lady, I should not have known how to joke about such a matter." Nothing he could say in words, no promise he could make her, would advance his suit in the least. He would never be granted any favors that way. He couldn't think how to move her.

A flush of crimson spread over his face. His eyes filled with tears. The skin of his face was splotched, here white and here crimson. The lady could not help but notice that he had not been misrepresenting his heart's intent. She also knew that men's confusion did not always necessarily arise from their defenseless hearts. Of course, it was in his favor that he let the lady see his tears at that time. She had not thought he could be so distressed.

"Sir," she said, "by God, it is not right that I give my love to you or to any other man when I have my own lord and gallant knight husband who does me homage very well and pays me every honor."

"Oh, Lady," he said, "of course he does! On my word, he must be a very happy man! But if gentleness and pity and sincerity ever made you feel affection for me, no one who reads or sings of love would hold you any lower because of it. Thus you would be loving me only by doing honor to the customs of our century. You could compare the alms you would thus so bestow to the worth of a voyage to the Holy Land."

"Now you are wishing me away from you," she said. "No. It would be wrong of me. I cannot suffer nor allow my heart to be so pledged to you in any manner. Now since your prayers are bootless, I beg you to desist."

"Oh!" he cried. "Now you have struck me dead, Lady. Please stop. Do not say more for any reason at all. Instead, treat me courteously and kindly. Retain me in your service by some jewel or some sash or some ring, where you will accept one from me in exchange. And I assure you that there will be nothing a knight could do for a lady, even, so help me God, if I were to lose my soul, that I would not do for you.

"Your green eyes and your bright face can rule me so effortlessly. I am entirely—just as I am—under your dangerous spell."

"Sir," she replied, "I don't care to have the reputation without the advantage. I am perfectly well aware of the fact that you are everywhere considered chivalrous; that reputation has been generally acceded to you for some time now. I would be very disillusioned if I allowed you to walk the road to my heart when I knew all along that my heart was not on it. That would be an ugly way for me to behave. It is a great sign of courtesy for whoever can to avoid censure."

"Everything you say only shows that you must want to help me, Lady," he said, "If you were to let me die because you wouldn't love me, then that would be a blot on your name, if that lovely face of yours, so full of frankness, were to commit homicide. In any case, we must come to some conclusion soon. Lady of beauty, so endowed with all earthly good, in God's name, look to it!"

His polite and pleasant words caused the lady to fall to the point of wanting to hear his pleas. She did feel sorry for him, for she no longer believed that his sighs and the tears he shed were insincere. From that moment she told herself that Love perforce must be torturing him sorely. It must be Love which forced him to do what he was doing. She also realized that if she were to take a lover, she never could find another so chivalrous as this knight. She still could not help but wonder at all those things he had said and which no one but him had ever said to her before— not ever before that very day. . . . Along with this thought, or rather contrary to it, came another line of reasoning: she should keep from committing herself to something she might later have occasion to repent.

While he was in great pain to know what she was thinking and into what part of her thoughts she had wandered, Love showed him a very pretty way to make a subtle and gallant move. In so many other difficult situations has Love shown his wisdom and his concern for those he has embarked.

While the gentle lady sat lost in her thoughts, the knight carefully slipped her ring from her finger and promptly replaced it with his. By this quick thinking he was to do something very advantageous. Then he interrupted her thoughts so completely that she was not able immediately to concern herself for the ring on her finger. Before she even had time to look down, he rose and said loudly, "Lady, give me your leave to depart. Know henceforth that my services and my self are both at your command."

He almost ran across the hall and down the steps, taking both his companions along with him. No one but him understood the motive behind this sudden departure. Sighing and pensive, he walked across the courtyard to his horse and mounted.

She whom he had most wanted to convince of the joys of love was left suddenly alone. "Has he really gone away?

What sort of manners is this? No knight ever behaved like this! I thought an entire year, he said, was less long than one day, and yet he has gone away and left me after such a short visit! Oh! just think if I had pledged myself to him by word or by gesture! Everybody would doubt him and should henceforth doubt all the false words such as he said here. Who could believe him just because of a few tears, or for a few false sighs he heaved? May the Holy Ghost come to my aid, but he hasn't lost a thing here! Nobody ever put on such a show, and that's the least I can say. I have to hand it to him."

As she said this to herself, the lady glanced down at her hands and so saw the ring. All the blood in her body rushed from her ring finger to her toes. It was a wonder she didn't faint. She was so amazed that she couldn't believe it. Her face became crimson. Then it grew deathly pale. "What's this?" she cried. "God save me, but don't I see the ring that was his? Either I am out of my mind, or I saw it on his finger just a few minutes ago. He must have done it, but how? And why did he take my ring? He is not my lover, but now I am sure he thinks he is. In any case, as God is my witness, he is a past master in the art of love; and I don't know where he learned it. . . . And how did it happen that he was able to take my ring?

"Just because I was so preoccupied that I wasn't thinking about guarding my ring, and just because he somehow managed to slip his ring on my finger, now he will say that he is my lover. . . . Will it be true? . . . Am I his true love? . . . Certainly not. That would be absolute madness. Surely he wouldn't for all the world say such a thing! . . . I shall send word for him to come instantly and speak with me. If he wants to keep me for a friend, then I shall tell him to take back his ring. . . . I don't believe he would dare defy me, unless he wants me to hate him."

The lady ordered a valet to mount and come to her at

267

once. Her maidens hurried to do her commands. A valet, ready to ride, came running in to her. "Boy," she said, "now ride, and fast! Spur after that knight! Say to him, as he holds my respect dear, that he is not to proceed forward, but that he is to return here immediately. He is to speak with me of the matter we have at hand."

"Lady," he said, "I will surely give him your message to the letter." Then the valet set out after the knight, sparing neither crop nor spur, after him whom love was tormenting. He caught up with him and headed him off in less than a league from the castle. Know that the knight, because of the lady's commandment, considered himself to have been born under a lucky star. He did not, however, ask the messenger why he had been ordered to return. He knew, of course, that it was because of the ring she wore on her finger. This would be her desire to ask for her ring. He modified his direction, for he desired very much to see the lady again. The messenger was very familiar with all the roads to the castle.

And oh, Lord, but he was happy to return, except for the suspicion he had that she might want to return his ring! "I can't believe that she is angry with me," he thought, "because of what I did." The joy he felt on the return trip more than covered his doubts. He rode down all the roads there were towards the fortress.

In spite of herself the lady had already gone out of her hall towards the front of the castle. Then, step by step, she had descended the staircase of honor. Lost in thought and thoughtlessly, she had then gone into the courtyard to while away the time. On her finger she saw the ring which she intended to return to the knight. It shone. "Even if he hasn't yet put me in any danger," she said, "if he does not want to take back his ring, I won't go so far as to pull his fine hair just for that. If I can, I will lead him over to this well, and there I will speak to him. If he does not want to take it without any fuss and bother, I will break off our conversation. . . . How? I won't be so silly as to throw his ring down right here in the middle of the pavement. Instead I will toss it somewhere where no one will see it. Perhaps that will be the well. In the future I shall consider anything upsetting that is said to me as nothing but a dream.

"Haven't I already spent many years as a faithful wife, without any infidelity towards my husband? Now this man through his chivalry already wants me, right at our very first interview, to become his love. And if I had done it, see how he already would have been undeserving."

Meanwhile the knight had already entered the castle courtyard, entirely unsuspecting of the lady's real state of mind. He saw her waiting anxiously. He saw her start towards him. Dismounting with a leap, he ran across the courtyard towards her just like a knight towards his true love. Neither his two companions nor anyone of the castle servants hindered him.

"Oh, faith! What a good outcome is there today, my Lady, to whom I am and always shall be!" Nor had he ever spoken to her in other terms. She had already that day heard so many words that touched her heart very nearly.

"Sir," she said, "let us stay outside. Let us walk over to this well and sit here for our delight."

Thus far the knight could see no signs adverse to himself in what she had said. Then, too, she had so sweetly walked forward to greet him. He thought that in truth he had won her love and her good graces because of the ring. However, he was still not sufficiently convinced that he could exult; before he could sit down he heard something that displeased him.

"Sir," she said, "tell me, I beg you, if this is your ring which I see here, and why you left it recently with me."

"Sweet lady," he replied, "when I leave the second time, you will still have it. I will tell you—this you may know—if you will not consider it a falsehood—the ring is now worth twice what it was for having been on your finger. If it pleased you, even my enemies could know by this summer that you have taken me for your true love, and I you."

"God's name," she said, "that is not so. Rather anything else. I shall never take a step from this house, so help me God, while I am still alive, when you have either the fame or the name of my love, for anything that I may see. You have not acted chivalrously in this matter; thus you have strayed too far from propriety. Look here, I want you to have your ring. It does not suit me at all. You shall not call me your love to my sorrow because I have had it in my possession."

Then he who had thought that he had conquered all despaired and was desolate. "My worth would be greatly diminished if what I hear is true. From this moment I shall feel no joy that does not turn itself instantly into grief."

"Now how, Sir," she asked, "can you possibly have either shame or annoyance from me to whom nothing, neither love nor lineage, binds you? I see no great outrage in the fact that I merely wish to return your ring. It is perfectly proper for you to take it back again since I have no right to it. I cannot keep it. I do not wish to take you as my lover because of the misconduct involved."

"God," he said, "if I were to drive a knife blade through my thigh, it would not cause me anywhere near the pain that your words cause me. How cruel is a person to confound and destroy another when that person has the whip hand. The forces of love bear down on me too hard; because of you they run full tilt against me and cause me great distress. There is nothing anyone can do which would make me take it back. In faith, may God never take me to my promised reward if I take it from you! You shall keep it and I shall leave you my heart also in your service. There is no device I could imagine which would show you so well how

I am your servant as this one of the ring and my heart."

She said, "Speak no more of it, for were you to make me against my will assume such an engagement with you, then you will have lost both my acquaintance and my permission to approach my presence. It is fitting, therefore, that you take back your ring."

"Not so."

"Even so. There's no more to be said. Or else you are much more than a lord, or else your importunities amount to physical force, or else you want to use force to make me retain it, in spite of myself. . . . Here. Take your ring. . . . I shall never want to keep it."

"Yes, you will."

"No, I won't."

"Yes, you will."

"Do you try to force me, sir?"

"Not in the least, sweet love. I am perfectly well aware that such great power I do have . . . not. And I am very sorry because of it, so help me God. Never more would any misfortune or bereavement touch me, and this I firmly believe, if you were only willing to grant me a small crumb of comfort."

"You might as well beat your head against this stone until you finally beat enough sense into it to see that you are to take back your ring."

"I see," said he, "that you are trying to teach me another tune. . . . I'd let them slip the hangman's noose about my neck first."

There is no point in holding a longer brief on this subject. There was just no taking back, and that's all there was to it.

"Sir," she said, "now I am convinced that no matter what I say to you, it only makes you rant all the more. No words can lead you to taking back your ring. Therefore I shall implore you once more—upon the respect you owe me—I pray you to take back your ring, if you hold my love dear."

From this web there was only one exit: now he had to take it back. Otherwise, she would say that his love for her was untrue and deceitful.

> *"Diex!" fet il, "li quels de ces. II.*
> *M'est or partis li mains mauvais?*
> *Or sai je bien, se je li lais,*
> *Qu'ele dira je ne l'aime mie. . . ."*

"God," he said to himself, "which of these two solutions is the less bad? Now I know well that if I leave it with her, she will say that I do not love her at all. Now we are splitting hairs very finely, so fine that I am treading so narrow a thread, am so squeezed by my own protestation of love that my own honor and chivalry require me to take it back, unless I wish to break faith with this beloved and honored lady. She has implored me and put me on my honor to do so in the name of Love. When I shall have put it back on my finger, then hers will be back where it was. If I do what she requests, then I shall lose her respect. There is no such thing, on the other hand, as a lover who refuses to do the bidding of his lady. And know that he who leaves some part of her desires undone does not love her. I must find a way to solve this without disobeying her commandment, for it must not be otherwise."

He still did not qualify the ring when he said, "Lady, I will take *it* according to my oath of love which obliges me to fulfill your wishes. At least *it* has been on your finger, which I see is so lovely."

"And I return your ring on condition that you acknowledge it."

The gentle knight remained pleasant, neither angry nor hateful. With a heart all on fire with love, he very pensively took the ring and sat sadly looking at it. Then he said, "My very great thanks to you! I see that the gold has not turned black for having been on your pretty finger."

The lady, thinking that he was going to slip the ring on his finger, began to smile. She had won. He, however, had already decided upon an alternate course of action which was to turn out very joyfully for him. He leaned over the well, which was only nine feet deep, and where he could not help but see—so pure and clear was the water—the shadow of the lady he loved more than anything in the world.

"Know," he said, "that I will not bring it back to you until I have bestowed it upon my sweetheart whom I love the most after you."

"My God!" she cried, "There's nobody here but us. Where did you find another love so quickly?"

"On my soul," he replied, "you shall very shortly see the noble and gentle lady who shall have this ring."

"Where is she?"

"In God's name, see her there. Your lovely shadow waits for it."

He took the ring in the tips of his fingers and held it out towards her in the well. "Since my lady does not want it, you will take it from me without any argument." As the ring struck the water, its surface was broken into little waves. When the mirror had become still again, he said, "Look, Lady. She took it. Now my stock has gone up in the world since she wears something that comes from you. For you know, if there were gates and doors down there that she could open, she would come up here and say me a very sweet thank you for the honor I have done her."

Well, my God, wasn't he a talented fellow in the art of chivalrous love! . . . From that very instant no article of his suit was unpleasing to the lady! All springtime and aglow, she cast her eyes into his. The returns on an investment in courteous love are great—when a man has such talent.

273

"Here was this man begging so long and suing for my love, and now he is so close to having it all! There never was, neither before his time nor after, since Adam bit into the apple, such great courtliness in a man. I don't know how he remembered it. When for love of my shadow he threw his ring into the well, I could not in all duty and can not any longer deny him the reward of my love. I don't know why I demurred so long. Never was there a man so good and so handsome who conquered love with a ring. Never was there a knight who more deserved to be loved."

Know that she did not wound him when she said aloud, "Sweet and dear love, your sweet words and your pleasant deed and the gift which to honor me you bestowed upon my shadow have put my whole heart in yours. Now please put my ring on your finger. Here, I give it to you with my love. I am sure that you will never love it less than your own, were it ever so much less pretty."

"The crown of the whole empire," he replied, "could not make me so happy."

Great was their bliss there on the edge of the well, as great as it could be. They kissed and kissed until they were satisfied, and the sweetness sank into their hearts. Their eyes did not throw their role far away, but then it was the turn of their hands. In the dance of the hands both he and the lady were artful. But as for the game which could not be done right then, it also would become them well.

It isn't suitable for that Jehan Renart to concern himself further with their relationship. If he hasn't anything else to say, he will do well to turn his thoughts elsewhere. For since their understanding and their love have molded their two hearts into one, as far as those events that remain in their lives are concerned, they will come to a head together, it seems to me. So as of this time today, I fall silent. Here ends *The Lay of a Shadow*.

Recount it—you who know numbers.

NOTES ON THE SOURCES

I. The Life of Saint Alexis

This is a complete translation of *The Life of Saint Alexis*.
It was made from the manuscript called L, of Hildesheim,
Germany, now in the Bibliothèque Nationale in Paris. Al-
though L was written in England in the twelfth century,
the poem itself appears to be a translation from Latin into
Old French, the original Old French version probably
dating from about 1040. Manuscript L was first printed in
Paris in 1872 by Gaston Paris. There are three other
manuscripts of *The Life of Saint Alexis* in the Bibliothèque
Nationale.

It has been said that the life of Alexis was among the
most popular and widespread stories in the Middle Ages.
The legend appears to have come originally from the
Orient, more particularly from the city of Edessa in Meso-
potamia where the Roman Emperor Valerian was defeated
by the Persians in 260 A.D. By the end of the next three
hundred years Edessa had become a center of the Christian
faith within the Byzantine Empire. There are versions of
the Alexis legend in Syrian, Greek, Georgian, Armenian,
German, and Scandinavian, as well as in Latin and the
Romance languages. In England there are Syrian manuscripts at least 1500 years old. In all versions, however,
Alexis is called "the man of God."

When the Crusaders captured Edessa in 1097, the legend
was then six hundred years old, since Alexis would have
lived in the fifth century. From Edessa the legend passed

into Greece, where valuable literary modifications were made. Alexis' mother was given the name of Aglaé and the story was treated in narrative poetry and in hymns. Also in Greece the life of Alexis seems to have been combined with that of another saint named John. Here too Alexis is transferred from "eastern Rome" or Constantinople to the western Rome in Italy. The subsequent Latin versions have Alexis interred at Saint Peter's in Rome.

The Old French version translated here is by an unknown author. His language is simple, but its effect is pathetic, thin, and even cruel. He wrote in stanzas of five lines each, without rhyme, but with the verses assonanced, as:

[vs. 1]   *Bons fut li secles al tens ancienur*
           quer feiz i ert e justise ed amur
           si ert creance dunt or n i at nul prout
           tut est mudez, perdud ad sa colur
           ia mais n iert tel com fut as anceisurs.

II.   The Romance of Girart de Viene

The translation given here is a summary of a very long tale, *The Romance of Girart de Viene*. The text used for translation and summary was that of the French manuscript in the Bibliothèque Nationale (Ms. fr. 1448), published at Rheims in 1850 by Prosper Tarbé. Some corrections were made according to the reading of an English manuscript (20 BXIX) published in New York by Frederic G. Yeandle in 1930. There are in all five manuscripts of this romance, two in France and three in England.

In this case the author is known; he is Bertrand de Bar-sur-Aube, also the author of a second story called *Aymeri de Narbonne*. He appears to have been a friend and debtor of the House of Viene, of which he celebrates the heroism and renown. There is some historical basis for his narrative concerning Girart. There was an eleventh-century insurrection in which the Dukes of Burgundy refused to swear homage to the King of France. Our author attributes this revolt to the famous kiss, but that seems to have been the author's invention, and very proud of it he is. The reader will have noted how frequently the author retells the incident of the kiss. Medieval readers would have situated this romance against the mountain passes of the Pyrenees where *The Song of Roland* took place.

The present summary tells the story from the beginning to the end of Stanza LXXX (Yeandle edition) or through the first half of p. 73 of Tarbé's edition of 181 pages. It ends at the point where the nameless queen makes her exit.

The French manuscript begins:

[vs. 1]   *Bone chanson plait vos que ge voz die*
De haute ystoire et de grant baronie?
Millours ne puet estre ditte n'oïe:
Ceste n'est pas d'orgueil ne de folie,
De traïson, ne de losangerie,
Mais dou bernage que Jhésu benoie,
Dou plus très fier, qui onques fust en vie.

III.   The Swan Knight

Le Chevalier au Cygne, or *The Swan Knight,* is among the last of the eighty *chansons de geste* composed in France during the three centuries following the First Crusade. The present translation was made from the Belgian manuscript, No. 814 of the *Bibliotheca Belgica manuscripta* in Brussels. It was published in Brussels in 1846 by Baron de Reiffenburg, along with a Latin version of the same story, in Vol. I of *Le Chevalier au Cygne.*

The hero of the story, Godefroid de Bouillon, came from Belgium or Lower Lorraine, and not from France. His place

277

in the First Crusade was a prominent one since he was a leader in the successful capture of Jerusalem on July 15, 1099. He is also famous for having refused the title of King of Jerusalem. He was in his lifetime the Duke of Bouillon, but the story gives him a most legendary and illustrious ancestry. The glorification of the hero seems to have been the author's chief purpose. The thirteenth-century author is unknown.

The language of the poem is rude and abrupt, without ornamentation or description. It is well suited to a poem that is crude and coarse. The legendary material concerning the swan, although mentioned in 1187 by Guillaume de Tyr, is very much older than that date, and the author's ingenuity in attributing it to his hero is admirable. There are also other very old associations or symbols in this poem. One is the fountain or spring where the young King Oriant meets the maiden Béatrix. Another is the children's donning their swan shifts and returning to water and to marshes. The legend of the swan reappears in *Lohengrin*. Aside from his use of myth, the author introduces a great deal of realism into the poem.

Since the entire poem has 3476 verses, only fragments giving the main events of the story have been translated here. The portions included are vss. 1-2299, vss. 2371-2584, vss. 2677-2888, and a short conclusion.

IV. — V.   Eliduc *and* Yonec

The author who is called Marie de France—from her own words, "I am named Mary and am from France"—wrote towards the end of the twelfth century. Her literary career could have overlapped that of Chrétien de Troyes. Scholars have conjectured that she was of Norman French birth and that she lived in England, perhaps at the court of King Henry II. Aside from many fables and a work on

Saint Patrice, she is known and famous because of a group of poems she called *lais*. The word meant free narrative poem of indeterminate length. The verse is octosyllabic, arranged in rhyming couplets. Her longest *lai* is *Eliduc*, which comprises 1184 verses. The most famous is *Laustic*, or *The Nightingale*, which is only 160 verses. One *lai* about Tristran, a poem she called *Chèvrefeuille*, or *Honeysuckle*, is only 118 lines long. Each poem tells a love story.

In her *lais*, Marie de France dealt entirely with material from Celtic legends. She did this by her own choice and admission. Her works are therefore in a sense peripheral to the *Mabinogion* and to the subjects treated by Chrétien de Troyes. Sometimes, as in *Yonec* (562 verses), she follows an older myth very closely. At other times she is simply a novelist retelling a good story in her own fashion.

Her works and their purpose have been greatly disputed. She has been called both consciously and unconsciously anti-Christian. French scholars have been at a loss to reconcile her frequent references to piety with the immorality of her subjects. In fact, this author is not a moralist. When she comments, it is usually in favor of the lovers. No one knows who she was—court poet, troubadour, or wealthy lady. Her classical education is apparent, and her poetic talent indisputable.

Since she is the first woman writer, both a poet and novelist, in the French language, scholars have seen her as the literary ancestor of Marguerite de Navarre in the sixteenth century. Her principal theme was also love, as was that of Mme. de Lafayette in the seventeenth century and Claudine de Tencin in the eighteenth century. One could also place George Sand and Collette in this tradition. Although the two *lais* I have retold here are named after men, they are really focused primarily upon women. Marie de France seems, therefore, more closely related to such French women writers as Christine de Pisan in the fifteenth century and Mme. Simone de Beauvoir in our own day—both ardent and spirited champions of women.

It is true that she is neither a psychologist nor a moralist. She does not care why Eliduc fell in love with Guilliadun; it is enough for her to know that he did. She makes no attempt to generalize or to draw conclusions. What happened to Eliduc happened once and to him. Whether or not he was reprehensible does not seem to interest her either: the reader may be shocked at the nonchalant way in which the author disposes of the superstitious sailor in *Eliduc*. This sort of unconcern has worried scholars, some of whom have wanted to see in her a Celtic bard knowingly spreading resistance to Christianity.

The stories of Marie de France come from the mind; they are imagined, rather than inspired by observation. The visual imagery is at a minimum. What did our author see in her lifetime? What pictures has she shown? Very few. A party of knights riding up to Excester who are seen from a height. A silver city surrounded by water, where large ships tie up—some memory of Saint-Malo, perhaps. A sarcophagus covered with a golden mantle. A falcon mewed. . . . This paucity of images leads me to believe that Marie de France was a recluse, perhaps a nun. She saw very little. Her stories come from books; her knowledge of love is a dream knowledge. *Yonec* is a dream. One can be sure of it from the references to the tunnel of death, to the River Styx, and to the green meadow of the Elysian Fields, and doubly sure from the image of sleeping knights waiting to be reborn.

There are six good manuscripts containing some or all of the twelve *lais* of Marie de France: H and C in the British Museum and S, P, and Q in the Bibliothèque Nationale. Manuscript A contains all twelve *lais*. It was published in France by Roquefort in 1832. My translation follows this manuscript.

VI. The Romance of Tristran

The Tristran story here translated comes from the earliest known French version, dating from about 1150. The author is named Bérox or Béroul. All that remains of his original work is thirty-two folios, or 4485 verses, in a manuscript in the Bibliothèque Nationale (Ms. fr. 2171). This manuscript, made about 1250, has been badly damaged. Lines are also omitted and transposed. The beginning of the story, the end, and many lines in the middle are entirely missing or so damaged as to be illegible. The handwriting is that of one person, described as being heavy, cramped, and careless. Manuscript 2171 was published in Paris in 1835-1838 by Francisque Michel, and it has been reprinted many times since that date.

Nothing is known about Béroul except that he wrote a type of Old French called Anglo-Norman. It is not known whether he invented the adventures he recounted, whether he retold them, whether he based his version upon a lost, earlier work, and whether or not he was a professional *jongleur*. Since main elements occur prominently in his version, it is surmised that he followed closely an original Celtic tale or legend. Béroul's version is apparently meant to be read aloud because there are frequent exhortations to the listeners ("Lords!"), and also several recapitulations of the story.

A second account of Tristran, more polished and more learned, is that by an Anglo-Norman poet named Thomas; it dates from about 1180. It differs from the version of Béroul in that Thomas retold the story according to the precepts of courtly love. The story of Tristran is probably the single most important landmark in the medieval literature of love. It is a mysterious, compelling, and memorable tale.

In the present translation, only the material in vss. 1351-

1655, vss, 1774-2100, and vss, 2123-2932 is given. These verses contain what seem to be the essential passages of this version.

VII.   Erec and Enide

There are in Paris seven manuscripts of *Erec and Enide,* none of which is the original. The best two manuscripts, least carelessly written and most legible, are P and H. This romance was published in Paris in 1856 by Francisque Michel and three times in Germany between 1890 and 1909 by Wendelin Foerster, who collated the seven manuscripts.

The author is Chrétien de Troyes, who also wrote a *Tristran* which has not been found. Two other famous novels by him are *Cligès* and *Yvain*. In addition, Chrétien left two unfinished works: *Perceval* and *Le Chevalier de la Charette*—the latter was translated by Sir Thomas Malory. The Arthurian legends form the major source for Chrétien. This poet lived during the last part of the twelfth century at the court of Count Henry I of Champagne, who died at Jerusalem in 1191. His wife, Countess Marie of Champagne, was the patroness of Chrétien.

The writing techniques of Chrétien are far more varied than those of any other novelist of the Middle Ages, except perhaps for Béroul and Guillaume de Lorris. There is an excellent use of tenses, past tenses for narrative sections, and the present tense for accelerated action. The conversations between all the characters are vivid, realistic, and dramatic. The actual tone and words are skillfully captured. Enide's dialogues with herself are most effective in the original. She wonders whether she should warn her lord of danger:

> *Dirai li donc tot an apert?*
> *Nenil. Por quoi? Je n'oseroie,*
> *Que mon seignor correceroie.*

282

Psychologist and moralist Chrétien surely was. In addition, he was a practical and worldly man with a good knowledge of custom and manner. He was very much impressed by wealth, money, prestige, and the nobility. He knew to a penny the value of a horse, a gown, or a dinner, and how much a first-rate coronation, such as that of Erec at the end of the romance, would cost.

Erec and Enide comprises 6958 verses of octosyllabic couplets. The part retold here extends from verses 2474-4938. This section was chosen because it demonstrates the author's keen knowledge of psychology.

VIII.   The Romance of the Châtelain of Coucy

The *Romance of the Châtelain of Coucy* is a long poem consisting of 8244 octosyllabic verses in rhyming couplets. It is anonymous because, as the author tells us in the last lines, there would be no point in our knowing his name. He also says, however, that his name is concealed in the rhymes. He writes this work in honor of the lady he loves and will love to his dying day.

There was, a hundred years earlier, a real lyric poet named the Châtelain of Coucy who may have died in the Holy Land. Whether or not he sent his heart to the Lady of Fayel, or to any other lady, is a disputed point. Aside from such historical considerations, this romance has at least two intriguing innovations. The idea of an author using as a fictional character a real poet whose songs he can incorporate appropriately into the narrative is most original. Also, in the letter which the Châtelain on the point of death sends to his lady, which has been literally rendered here, he closely imitates the lyric style and the images of the real poet—Châtelain.

Our author would, indeed, be difficult to identify because he writes so limpidly that he eludes detection. He seems to have no favorite expressions, such as one sees at once in Bertrand de Bar-sur-Aube or in Adenès le Roi, both well-known writers of the thirteenth century. Our author is much better educated, less frivolous, less precious, more refined and gentlemanly. He appears also to be a thoughtful man and a good psychologist. He usually remains anonymous throughout the story, telling his narrative from the distant third person and past tense. When he comes to the subject of love itself, however, then he changes to the first person. Certain passages are beautiful, such as the hero's last words to his lady whom he must leave:

[v. 7260]   *En ce me reconfertoray,*
            Car bien voy plus de confort n'ay;
            Ne ciez confors ne me foura,
            Ne cilz espoirs ne changera,
            Se li uns de nous ne trespasse
            Devant le saison et l'espasse
            Que de vous departis seray.

The section here translated comes from the one manuscript in the Bibliothèque Nationale as printed and translated into modern French by G. A. Crapelet in 1829. Verses 1-3727, telling how the Châtelain fell in love, finally overcame the resistance of the Lady of Fayel, and established their liaison, have been omitted.

IX.   The Romance of the Story of the Grail

There is only one manuscript of the Grail story as told by Master Robert de Boron early in the thirteenth century, Ms. fr. 20047 in the Bibliothèque Nationale. It was first published by Francisque Michel in Paris in 1841, and again in 1861 by the Roxburghe Club in London. All that remains of the original poem of Boron are 3514 verses of octosyllabic couplets. The reader will note in parentheses a section missing from the Boron manuscript and supplied from a Latin prose translation of the thirteenth century.

The author is unknown except for his name. It has been suggested that he lived either in England at the court of King Henry II, or at the place he himself mentioned, Montbéliard in France. His work is unique, not so much from a literary or an artistic point of view, but for its ideas. Without ever mentioning Perceval, the author has given a background for his story and what seems to be its most satisfying explanation after the fact of the Grail legend itself. His version is in fact a synthesis, a linking and blending of authentic Roman history with Christian theology and Celtic legend. From frequent references to the New Testament, or New Covenant, as symbolized by the cup, the author moves to the origins of the Welsh people, the spread of Christianity, the reason for King Arthur's Round Table, and the meaning of the Siege Perilous.

Robert de Boron's poem is remarkable for its network of symbols: the Mass, the Trinity, the Ark of Judaism and the Fisher King. Also prominent are the doctrine of grace and the reasons for those excluded from the feast. Underlying this work is the theme of purity characteristic of Perceval.

Verses 152-193 are omitted from this translation, which includes vv. 1-152 and vv. 193-3500.

X. Aucassin and Nicolette

The French thirteenth century, called "the classical century," produced two romances that continue to be studied, read and reread, and translated again and again. These are the "chantefable" called *Aucassin and Nicolette,* and *Le Roman de la Rose* by Guillaume de Lorris. The latter work is best known to English readers through its translation by Geoffrey Chaucer.

Aucassin and Nicolette consists of forty-one sections of alternating poetry and prose. These sections of assonanced poetry of varying lengths are introduced in this complete translation by three dots; the prose passages are prefaced with a dash. Although the author is unknown, his language was identified by Suchier, in 1881, as being Picard. Although there have been many printings of it since 1752, there has so far been discovered only one manuscript, which is in the Bibliothèque Nationale (Ms. fr. 2168).

The author, who may be the "old prisoner" mentioned in the opening lines, seems to treat the idealization of women, the sacred order of knighthood, the adoration of purity, and the awe of riches and power with irony. His Nicolette is one of the first great heroines in French literature in the sense that she is a true woman and the mistress of her fate. It is almost entirely her story from start to finish. Youth and sex are glorified to some extent, and in this story "love makes the world go 'round." It defeats opposition, wins over obstacles, and triumphs in the end, as in a Hollywood movie. The whole story is told with a certain lightheartedness that has charmed readers through the centuries. The genial personality of the unknown author seems to shine through this work; he is playful and tender at the same time.

XI. The Lay of a Shadow

The Lay of a Shadow, or in French *Le Lai de l'Ombre,* is a thirteenth-century romance of 962 verses in octosyllabic couplets, with very skillful rhymes that are primarily consonantal. Although no original manuscript has been discovered, the French scholar Joseph Bédier deduced that it had been copied twenty-nine times. He found seven manuscripts, which he classified into three groups: **ABCG, DF,** and **E.** The critical edition of Bédier is the one used for this translation of the complete poem. The text is difficult, owing in part to the author's preciosity and plays upon words. Such obscurities exist in the first lines of the poem as well as in the last verse:

[v. 962]   *Contez, vous qui savez de nombre.*

The author's name, Jehan Renart, appears in the text. Nothing is known of him although both Bédier and Paris believed him to have been also the author of two other romances: *L'Escoufle* and *Guillaume de Dôle*. Bédier found the name *Renart* by reading backwards in vs. 3641 of the latter romance:

*Qu'il en*tra en *r*eligion.

One supposition is that the author became a monk. In any case, he seems to have come from northeastern France.

It is fascinating to theorize about this author because the stamp of his personality seems so strongly set upon his work. There are not only references to himself and to his ideas, but there is also a certain independent, decisive, and even aggressive manner about his way of writing that stimulates speculation. Both the author and his hero seem to have much in common. As one translates, one senses the presence of a very strong individual who was a clear and logical thinker and a somewhat cynical man.